Equivalent and
Equidecomposable Figures

V. G. Boltyanskii

Translated and adapted from the first Russian edition (1956) by

ALFRED K. HENN *and* CHARLES E. WATTS

SURVEY OF

RECENT EAST EUROPEAN MATHEMATICAL LITERATURE

A project conducted by

ALFRED L. PUTNAM *and* IZAAK WIRSZUP

*Department of Mathematics,
The University of Chicago, under a
grant from the National Science Foundation*

D. C. HEATH AND COMPANY   BOSTON

Physics-math

845110

THIS BOOKLET deals with a class of problems fundamental to the theories of area and volume. In the case of plane figures the central problem considered stems from the following question: If two polygons have equal areas, is it possible to dissect one of them into a finite number of parts which can be rearranged to form the other? The second part of the booklet is concerned with the analogous problem for solid figures. In view of the elementary nature of the topics themselves, it may seem surprising that some of the theorems proved in this booklet are the product of comparatively recent research.

For the first four chapters, the reader needs only the background of one year of algebra and a half-year of plane geometry. Solid geometry and trigonometry are needed for the last two chapters. Some of the proofs toward the end of the booklet are rather difficult, and on first reading the student may wish to learn only the statement of these theorems.

PREFACE TO THE AMERICAN EDITION

CONTENTS

Equivalent and Equidecomposable Figures

1. The Bolyai-Gerwin Theorem; Equidecomposability of Polygons

1. DECOMPOSITION METHOD

Let us examine the two figures represented in Fig. 1. All line segments making up the cross-shaped figure are of equal length, and the side of the square is equal to the line segment AB. The dotted lines shown in the illustration divide these figures into the

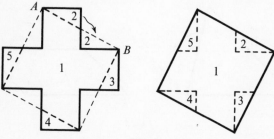

Fig. 1

same number of congruent parts (corresponding parts in the two figures are marked by the same numbers). This fact is expressed in words as follows: the figures represented in Fig. 1 are *equidecomposable*. In other words, *two figures are said to be equidecomposable if it is possible to decompose one of them into a finite number of parts which can be rearranged to form the second figure.*

It is clear that two equidecomposable figures have equal areas. On this is based a simple method for calculating areas, which is known as the *decomposition* method. This method (already known to Euclid more than 2,000 years ago) is as follows: In order to calculate the area of a figure, try to decompose the figure into a finite number of parts in such a way that these parts can be rearranged to form a simpler figure (whose area is already known).

We recall here some examples of the application of this method encountered in high school geometry. In Fig. 2 a method for calculating the area of a parallelogram is indicated: a parallelogram and a rectangle which have the same base and the same altitude

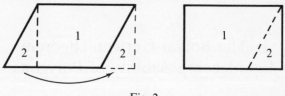

Fig. 2

are equidecomposable and, therefore, equal in area.[1] Similarly, Fig. 3 indicates how one might calculate the area of a triangle: the triangle has the same area as a parallelogram of the same base and half the altitude, because these two figures are equidecomposable.

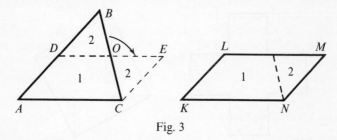

Fig. 3

Finally, in Fig. 4 a method is indicated for calculating the area of a trapezoid.

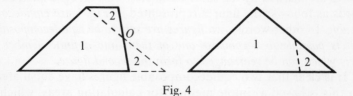

Fig. 4

---

[1] Notice, however, that such a simple method as splitting off one triangle does not always lead to the desired result. In the case shown in the accompanying figure, the parallelogram must be divided not into two but into more than two parts in order to enable one to build from them a rectangle having the same base and the same altitude (see below, the proof of Lemma 3).

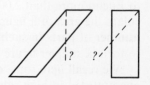

Of course, the problem of equidecomposability may be considered for curvilinear figures also (Fig. 5); however, we shall not deal with this type of figure here, but only with polygons.[1]

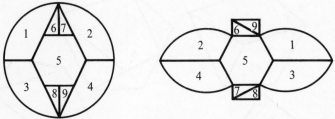

Fig. 5

Thus, all pairs of equidecomposable polygons have equal areas. It is natural to ask if the converse holds: if two polygons have equal areas, are they equidecomposable? An affirmative answer to this question was obtained (almost simultaneously) by the Hungarian mathematician Bolyai (1832) and the German officer and amateur mathematician Gerwin (1833). We shall now proceed to prove this theorem.

2. THE BOLYAI-GERWIN THEOREM

Before undertaking to prove this theorem, we shall prove some auxiliary propositions.

LEMMA 1. *If a figure A is equidecomposable with a figure B, and figure B is equidecomposable with a figure C, then figures A and C are also equidecomposable.* (See Fig. 6 on the next page.)

In figure B let us draw lines decomposing it into parts which may be rearranged so as to give figure A (solid lines in Fig. 6a); let us next draw lines which decompose figure B into parts which may be rearranged so as to give figure C (solid lines in Fig. 6b). These two sets of lines together decompose figure B into smaller parts.

[1] The problem of measuring the areas of curvilinear figures may be reduced by means of a limiting process to the problem of measuring the areas of polygons; it suffices here to recall the calculation of the area of a circle learned in plane geometry. For this reason, although we are restricting our attention to polygons, we are nevertheless considering the basis of the more fundamental questions of measuring areas. Similarly, in Chapters 5 and 6 we shall deal only with polyhedra; the problem of calculating volumes of solids with curvilinear surfaces will not be examined.

These smaller parts are numbered 1 to 8 in Fig. 6a and Fig. 6b, and it is clear that these smaller parts may be rearranged to give

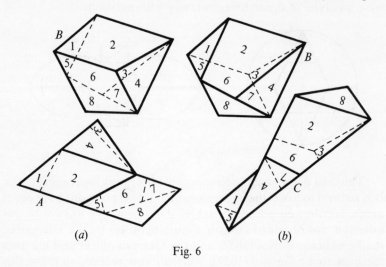

Fig. 6

either figure A or figure C. Thus, figures A and C are equidecomposable.

LEMMA 2. *Every triangle is equidecomposable with some rectangle.*

Let AB be the longest side[1] of the triangle ABC (Fig. 7), and let CD be the altitude from C to AB. The point D lies between A and B; otherwise, either ∠A or ∠B would be obtuse, and the side AB would not be the longest (Fig. 8). Through the mid-point of CD

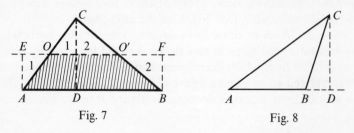

Fig. 7   Fig. 8

draw a straight line parallel to AB, and drop perpendiculars AE and BF to this line. The rectangle AEFB is equidecomposable with the triangle ABC. In fact, the triangles marked "1" in Fig. 7 are congruent, and those marked "2" are also. The two figures ABC

[1] That is, suppose neither of the other two sides of triangle ABC is longer.

4

and *AEFB* are each composed of a trapezoid, shaded in Fig. 7, and two triangles 1, 2.

LEMMA 3. *Two parallelograms which have a common base and the same area are equidecomposable.*

Let *ABCD* and *ABEF* be two parallelograms having a common base *AB* and the same area (Fig. 9). The altitudes of these paral-

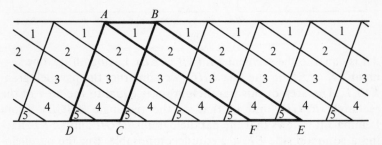

Fig. 9

lelograms are equal; hence, the segments *DC* and *FE* lie in a straight line. On the straight line *AB* lay off a series of line segments equal to *AB* and through the end points of each of these segments draw straight lines parallel to the lines *AD* and *AF*. The strip between the parallel straight lines *AB* and *DE* is thereby divided into a series of polygons (Fig. 9). Each of these polygons becomes superposed on a congruent polygon if displaced horizontally by a distance equal to the length of *AB*. (Prove this!) Congruent polygons are marked by the same numbers in Fig. 9. It must be noted that each of the parallelograms *ABCD* and *ABEF* contains one part marked "1," one part marked "2," and so on. Thus, these parallelograms are equidecomposable.[1]

LEMMA 4. *Two rectangles having equal areas are equidecomposable.*

Let *ABCD* and *EFGH* be two rectangles which are equal in area (Fig. 10). From among the four line segments *AB*, *BC*, *EF*, and *FG* choose the longest; suppose this is the line segment *AB*. The circle with radius *AB* and center *E* intersects the half-line *GH* in some

---

[1] If the sides *AF* and *BC* of the parallelograms *ABCD* and *ABEF* do not intersect, then Fig. 9 will take the form shown in the drawing here. It is then sufficient to cut off a triangle from the parallelogram *ABCD* in order to be able to construct the parallelogram *ABEF* from the two parts obtained (see footnote on page 2).

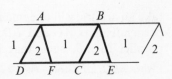

point L. (Since $AB \geq EH$, the circle of radius AB and center E will have a point in common with the straight line HG.) The segment

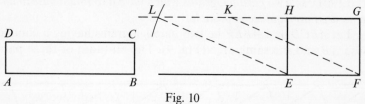

Fig. 10

AB is equal to the segment EL ($AB = EL$). Laying off the line segment $LK = EF$ on the line LHG, we construct the parallelogram $EFKL$. The area of this parallelogram is equal to the area of the rectangle $EFGH$ (and to that of the rectangle $ABCD$). From Lemma 3 it follows that the parallelograms $EFGH$ and $EFKL$, having a common side EF, are equidecomposable. But the parallelograms $ABCD$ and $EFKL$ have equal sides AB and EL. Therefore, by Lemma 3 they are also equidecomposable.[1] Finally, since the parallelogram $EFKL$ is equidecomposable with each of the rectangles $ABCD$ and $EFGH$, these last rectangles must also be equidecomposable with each other (Lemma 1).

LEMMA 5. *Every polygon is equidecomposable with some rectangle.*

Every polygon (whether it is convex or not) can be decomposed into a finite number of triangles (marked 1, 2, 3, ... in Fig. 11). Let us

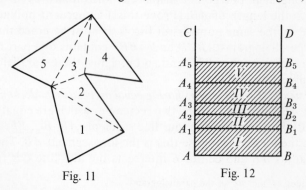

Fig. 11   Fig. 12

take an arbitrary line segment AB, and from its end points draw the perpendiculars AC and BD (Fig. 12). A line A_1B_1 is then drawn parallel to AB, such that the rectangle ABB_1A_1 has the same

[1] When $EFKL$ is rotated to make EL parallel to AB; see page 13.

6

area as triangle 1. Then triangle 1 and the rectangle ABB_1A_1 (marked by I) are equidecomposable. For according to Lemma 2, triangle 1 must be equidecomposable with some rectangle which is in turn equidecomposable with the rectangle I which has the same area (Lemma 4); therefore, triangle 1 and rectangle I are equi-decomposable (Lemma 1). Next draw the line segment A_2B_2 parallel to AB such that the rectangle $A_1B_1B_2A_2$ (marked by II) has the same area as triangle 2. Then triangle 2 and rectangle II are equi-decomposable. Next construct the rectangle III equidecomposable with triangle 3, etc. The rectangles I, II, III, ... thus constructed, together form a rectangle (shaded in Fig. 12), which by construction is equidecomposable with the original polygon.

We are now in a position to prove the theorem mentioned above.

THE BOLYAI-GERWIN THEOREM. *Two polygons which have equal areas are equidecomposable.*

Proof. According to Lemma 5 each of the polygons is equide-composable with some rectangle. The two rectangles obtained will have equal areas and will therefore be equidecomposable (Lemma 4). Thus, the two original polygons are equidecomposable by Lemma 1.

Remark. The term "polygons" in the Bolyai-Gerwin theorem need not necessarily be taken to mean a section of a plane bounded by a *single* closed broken line. The theorem holds also for more complex figures bounded by several closed broken lines (Fig. 13). Actually, the only characteristic property of "polygons" used in

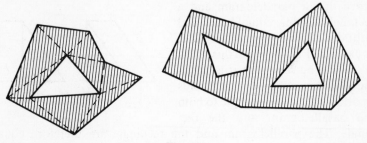

Fig. 13

the proof of Lemma 5 is that they can be dissected into triangles. But this is a property possessed by any figure bounded by closed broken lines (Fig. 13).

3. COMPLEMENTATION METHOD

Instead of the decomposition method, it is often convenient to use another method for calculating areas, a "dual" method. This method is called the *complementation* method, and we shall now proceed to examine it. Instead of decomposing figures into congruent parts, we shall now add congruent parts to two figures in such a way that the new figures are congruent. Consider the figures shown in Fig. 1. They have equal areas, since they are equidecomposable, but the equality of their areas may also be proved in a different way (Fig. 14). By adding four congruent triangles to both the cross and

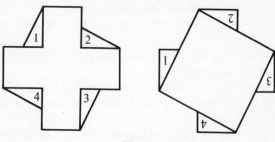

Fig. 14

the square, we obtain one and the same figure. Hence, it follows that the two original figures (the cross and the square) have equal areas.

The complementation method may be applied successfully to prove theorems of elementary geometry. For instance, in order to prove that a parallelogram and a rectangle having equal bases and altitudes also have equal areas, let us examine Fig. 15. From this drawing it can be seen that it is possible to obtain congruent trapezoids by adding the same triangle to both the parallelogram and the rectangle. The parallelogram and the rectangle are therefore equal in area.[1]

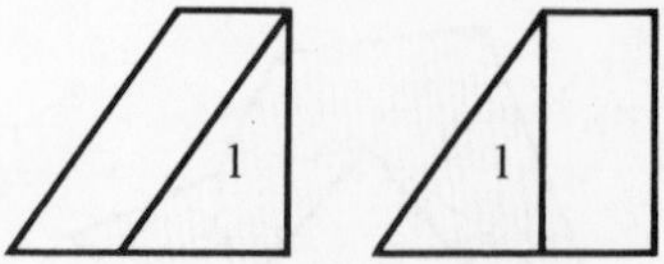

Fig. 15

---

[1] This method for calculating the areas of parallelograms is preferable to the usual method (Fig. 2). Actually, the method indicated in Fig. 15 should always be applied instead of the method indicated in Fig. 2 (see the footnote on page 2).

Using this same method, the Pythagorean theorem is easily proved. Let ABC be a right triangle. In order to prove that the area of square I constructed on the hypotenuse is equal to the sum of the areas of the squares II and III constructed on the legs (Fig. 16), let us examine Fig. 17. From this drawing we see that it is pos-

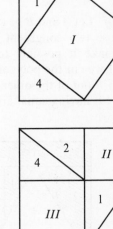

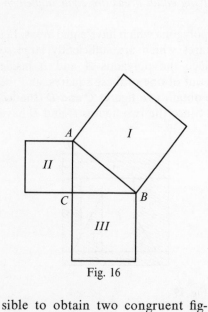

Fig. 16

Fig. 17

sible to obtain two congruent figures—two squares whose sides are equal in length to the sum of the legs of the triangle ABC—by adding four triangles, each congruent to the triangle ABC, both to square I and to the sum of the squares II and III. Thus, the Pythagorean theorem is proved. For the sake of comparison we also give here a drawing which indicates how the Pythagorean theorem can be proved by means of the decomposition method (Fig. 18).

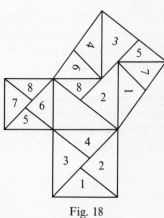

Fig. 18

9

We shall call two polygons *equicomplementable* if it is possible to obtain two congruent figures by adding congruent polygons to each. It is clear that equicomplementable figures have equal areas. It is natural to ask if the converse holds: if two polygons have equal areas, are they equicomplementable? An affirmative answer to this question is readily obtained by applying the Bolyai-Gerwin theorem as in the proof below.

THEOREM. *Two polygons having equal areas are equicomplementable.*

Proof. Let A and B be two polygons which have equal areas. Let us choose two congruent squares which are sufficiently large so as to make it possible to place the polygons A and B inside them. If we cut the polygon A out of one of these squares, and the polygon B out of the other, we obtain two figures C and D (shaded in Fig. 19) having equal areas. Since the two figures C and D have

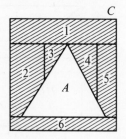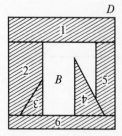

Fig. 19

equal areas, they are equidecomposable (by the Bolyai-Gerwin theorem). Consequently, figures C and D may be decomposed into pairs of congruent parts; this implies that the polygons A and B are equicomplementable.

The theorems in this chapter have shown that for plane polygons, equidecomposability and equicomplementability are each equivalent to having equal areas. As we shall see in Chapters 5 and 6 (where we shall be examining polyhedra), the situation is different for solid figures.

2. The Hadwiger-Glur Theorem

The Bolyai-Gerwin theorem shows that "equality of area" and "equidecomposability" are equivalent for polygons. This theorem opens up several possibilities for further investigation. In particular, there arises the interesting question: can additional conditions be imposed on the number or distribution of the parts which make up the polygons of equal area? A remarkable result of this type was obtained in 1951 by the Swiss mathematicians Hadwiger and Glur. They established that in the Bolyai-Gerwin theorem the additional condition may be imposed that the parts into which one of the two polygons of equal area is decomposed and the corresponding parts of

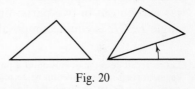

Fig. 20

the second polygon *have their corresponding sides parallel.* At first glance this result seems improbable; for example, it is difficult to see how two congruent triangles which have been rotated through an arbitrary angle relative to one another (Fig. 20) can be decomposed into congruent parts whose corresponding sides are parallel. Nevertheless, such a decomposition exists—not only for triangles but also for arbitrary polygons. The present chapter is concerned with a proof of this fact.

4. MOTIONS

Let us turn again to the proof for the Bolyai-Gerwin theorem given in the preceding chapter. In the proof for Lemma 3 (Fig. 9) the parallelogram *ABCD* was decomposed into a number of constituent parts (marked 1, 2, 3, ...) from which the parallelogram *ABEF* could be obtained. From Fig. 9 it is seen that in order to obtain the parallelogram *ABEF* it is sufficient to apply a parallel translation to the constituent parts; that is, it is sufficient to

11

displace each part along some line segment without rotation.[1] Specifically, the equidecomposability of the two parallelograms shown in Fig. 2 is established by means of parallel translations.

In order to establish the equidecomposability of the figures represented in Fig. 3 and 4, parallel translations are not sufficient; but it is readily shown that these figures are equidecomposable by using, in addition to parallel translations, also a reflection with respect to a point[2] (a "central symmetry"). If we replace the triangle *BOD* by the triangle *COE* (which is its reflection with respect to the point *O*) (Fig. 3), we obtain the parallelogram *ADEC*, which can then be made to coincide with the parallelogram *KLMN* by means of a parallel translation. The equidecomposability of the figures represented in Fig. 4 can be proved analogously. In the proof for Lemma 2 we also made use of central symmetries (Fig. 7).

Let us now recall the proof for Lemma 4 (Fig. 10). The proof of the equidecomposability of the rectangles *ABCD* and *EFGH* was carried out in two parts: first of all it was noted that the rectangle *EFGH* is equidecomposable with the parallelogram *EFKL*;

<hr />

[1] Let us recall here the definition of a parallel translation. Let $\overrightarrow{PQ}$ be a directed line segment (vector), its direction being marked in Fig. 21 by an arrow. From an arbitrary point *M* let us draw the line segment *MM'* equal and parallel to *PQ* and having the same direction. One then says that the point *M'* is obtained from *M* by a *parallel translation* with respect to $\overrightarrow{PQ}$. By subjecting all points of a figure *F* to such a transformation, a new figure *F'* is obtained, and one says that *F'* is obtained from *F* by a *parallel translation* with respect to $\overrightarrow{PQ}$. It is clear that in order to perform the inverse process, that is, to obtain the figure *F* from the figure *F'*, it is necessary to apply a parallel trans-

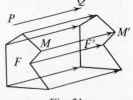

Fig. 21

lation with respect to $\overrightarrow{QP}$, which coincides with the line segment $\overrightarrow{PQ}$ but has the opposite direction. It may be noted here that the translation of *F* to the identical figure *F* may be regarded also as a parallel translation (a translation determined by a "zero line segment").

[2] Let us recall the definition of reflection with respect to a point (a central symmetry). Let *O* be a point (the center of symmetry). If *AA'* is a line segment whose mid-point is the point *O*, its end points *A* and *A'* are said to be *symmetric* with respect to the center *O*. If every point of a figure *F* is transformed into the point symmetric to it (with respect to *O*), a new figure *F'* is obtained. We say that *F* and *F'* are *centrally symmetric* to one another (with respect to the center *O*) and the transformation which carries one figure into the other is called a *central symmetry* (Fig. 22).

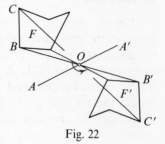

Fig. 22

then the equidecomposability of the latter parallelogram with the rectangle *ABCD* was established. The equidecomposability of the figures *EFGH* and *EFKL* can be established by using parallel translations alone (on the basis of Lemma 3, since the parallelograms *EFGH* and *EFKL* have a common base). Although the parallelograms *ABCD* and *EFKL* have equal sides *AB* and *EL*, these are not parallel, and in order to apply Lemma 3 the parallelogram *EFKL* must first be *rotated* so as to make the side *EL* parallel to *AB*. Thus, the proof given above for Lemma 4 involves the *rotation* of the figure *EFKL* (and, of course, of all its constituent parts) through a given angle.

It is seen that in the majority of cases examined in Chapter 1, the use of central symmetries and parallel translations alone is sufficient to establish the equidecomposability of the figures—with the exception of Lemma 4, the proof of which involves the rotation of the figure through an angle. The question naturally arises: is it possible to give a proof for Lemma 4 without using rotations? Is it possible, in general, to prove the equidecomposability of two arbitrary polygons having equal areas without having to rotate the constituent parts, that is, by means of central symmetries and parallel translations alone? In order to answer these questions it is necessary to study some of the properties of motions.

Parallel translations, central symmetries, and rotations are examples of motions.[1] An arbitrary motion may be represented as follows: a figure *F* is "lifted out" of its plane and transposed as a "rigid body" to a new position *F'*; this transposition from figure *F* to figure *F'* is called a *motion* (Fig. 23).[2] We shall denote motions by small letters.

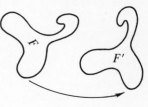

Fig. 23

For each motion *d* there is an inverse motion by means of which each figure is transposed from its new posi-

---

[1] Central symmetries are special cases of rotations: in order to replace a figure by its reflection with respect to a point, it is sufficient to rotate it about the center of symmetry through an angle of 180° (Fig. 22).

[2] In this case we are talking about the motion of a single figure (figure *F*). Frequently it is preferable to think in terms of a motion of the whole plane (together with all figures in it). For instance, "a parallel translation with respect to the line segment *PQ*" may be applied to every figure in the plane; that is, the *whole plane* is regarded as changing position; "a central symmetry with respect to a center *O*" also signifies a motion of the whole plane, etc.

tion, due to the motion d, back to its original position. For example, the inverse motion for a parallel translation with respect to $\overrightarrow{PQ}$ is a parallel translation with respect to $\overrightarrow{QP}$ (which has the opposite direction). The inverse motion for a central symmetry with respect to the point O is that same central symmetry. We shall formulate these remarks in a separate lemma.

LEMMA 6. *If the motion d is a parallel translation or a central symmetry, then the inverse motion corresponding to d will also be a parallel translation or a central symmetry.*

Motions may be carried out in succession—for instance, we may first apply a parallel translation with respect to some directed line segment (first motion), and then a central symmetry with respect to some point (second motion). If we first apply a motion d_1 and then a motion d_2 we obtain a new (resultant) motion which we shall denote by $d_1 \cdot d_2$; this new motion is called the *product* of the motions d_1 and d_2.[1]

LEMMA 7. *The product of two central symmetries with centers O_1 and O_2 is a parallel translation with respect to the directed line segment $2\overrightarrow{O_1O_2}$.*

Let the points A and A' be symmetric with respect to O_1, and let the points A' and A'' be symmetric with respect to O_2. Then O_1O_2 is a line segment joining the mid-points of two sides of the triangle $AA'A''$; that is, the line segment AA'' is parallel to the line segment O_1O_2 but twice as long (Fig. 24).[2] Thus, a parallel translation with

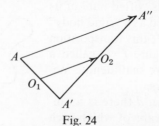

Fig. 24

respect to $\overrightarrow{PQ} = 2\,\overrightarrow{O_1O_2}$ takes an arbitrary point A to the same point A'' as the product of the central symmetries with respect to O_1 and O_2.

---

[1] Sometimes it is preferable to denote the resultant of the successive motions d_1 and d_2 by $d_2 \cdot d_1$, rather than by $d_1 \cdot d_2$.

[2] If the point A lies on the straight line O_1O_2, then the points A, A', A'' will be collinear; that is, the points do not determine a triangle. A verification of the conclusion in this case can be made by checking the special cases possible.

LEMMA 8. *The product of three central symmetries with centers* O_1, O_2, O_3 *is a central symmetry.*

Let O be a point such that the directed line segments $\overrightarrow{O_1O_2}$ and $\overrightarrow{OO_3}$ are equal, parallel, and oriented in the same direction (Fig. 25). Then the product of the symmetries with centers O_1, O_2 coin-

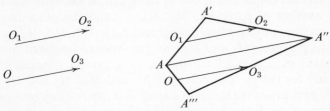

Fig. 25

cides with the product of the symmetries with centers O, O_3 (since it follows from Lemma 7 that both products are the parallel translation with respect to $2\,\overrightarrow{O_1O_2} = 2\,\overrightarrow{OO_3}$). Thus, instead of three central symmetries with respect to centers O_1, O_2, O_3, we may multiply the symmetries with respect to centers O, O_3, O_3, which evidently gives a single symmetry with respect to the center O (since applying successively two central symmetries with respect to the same center O_3 will result in each point returning to its original position).[1]

LEMMA 9. *If each of two motions d_1 and d_2 is either a parallel translation or a central symmetry, their product will also be a parallel translation or a central symmetry.*

Since a parallel translation is the product of two central symmetries (which follows readily from Lemma 7), the product of the motions referred to in the lemma can be represented as the product of two, three, or four central symmetries. But the product of two central symmetries is a parallel translation (Lemma 7); the product of three central symmetries reduces to a single central symmetry (Lemma 8); and the product of four central symmetries reduces to the product of two (since the product of three central symmetries is a single central symmetry), the product of these two being a parallel translation. In each case the product turns out to be either a central symmetry or a parallel translation.

[1] The fact that $(s_1 \cdot s_2) \cdot s_3 = (s \cdot s_3) \cdot s_3 = s \cdot (s_3 \cdot s_3) = s$ (where s_1, s_2, s_3, s stand for the central symmetries with respect to the centers O_1, O_2, O_3, O, respectively) is assumed in this proof. This "associative law" for multiplication of motions is verified in Property 4, section 10.

15

5. THE HADWIGER-GLUR THEOREM

We shall call a pair of polygons *S-equidecomposable*[1] if their equidecomposability can be established by means of parallel translations and central symmetries alone. In other words, two polygons are *S*-equidecomposable if one of them can be decomposed into a finite number of parts M_1, M_2, M_3, ..., and the other into the same number of respectively congruent parts M_1', M_2', M_3', ..., so that the polygons M_1 and M_1' can be obtained from one another by means of a parallel translation or a central symmetry, and similarly for the pairs of polygons M_2 and M_2', M_3 and M_3', etc.

We next prove the theorem stating that *any two polygons having equal areas are S-equidecomposable.* The proof of this theorem is completely analogous to that of the Bolyai-Gerwin theorem, and is based on similar lemmas.

LEMMA 1*a.* *If A and C are two polygons each of which is S-equidecomposable with the polygon B, then A and C are also S-equidecomposable.*

Decompose the polygon *B* into smaller polygons which may be rearranged (using parallel translations and central symmetries) to give polygon *A*; then decompose *B* into polygons which may be rearranged (using parallel translations and central symmetries) to give polygon *C* (Fig. 26). The two sets of lines introduced in form-

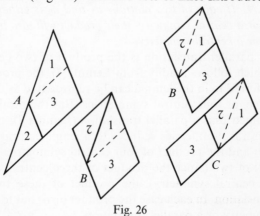

Fig. 26

ing these decompositions together decompose figure *B* into even smaller polygons. It is clear that both polygons *A* and *C* may be

[1] The meaning of this term will be analyzed in greater detail in section 11.

obtained by suitably rearranging these smaller parts, and that parallel translations and central symmetries suffice. Thus, the polygons A and C are dissected into smaller parts in some manner. Denote the parts of figure B by M_1', M_2', M_3', ..., the corresponding parts of polygon A by M_1, M_2, M_3, ..., and the corresponding parts of polygon C by M_1'', M_2'', M_3'', ... Each of the polygons M_1 and M_1'' is obtainable from M_1' by means of a parallel translation or a central symmetry. From this it follows (Lemma 6) that M_1' is obtainable from M_1 by means of a parallel translation or a central symmetry, and, therefore, the polygon M_1'' is obtainable from M_1 by means of a parallel translation or a central symmetry (Lemma 9). Analogously, the polygon M_2'' is obtainable from M_2 by means of a parallel translation or a central symmetry; the same is true of M_3 and M_3'', etc. Thus, the polygons A and C are S-equidecomposable.

It might be noted that only here are the properties of central symmetries and parallel translations examined above (Lemmas 6 and 9) actually applied.

LEMMA 2*a*. *Every triangle is S-equidecomposable with some rectangle.*

See the proof for Lemma 2, section 2. The triangles marked "1" in Fig. 7 are obtained from each other by means of a symmetry with respect to the center O, and the triangles marked "2" by means of a symmetry with respect to the center O'. Finally, the trapezoid which is shaded in Fig. 7 remains in the same position, that is, it undergoes a parallel translation with respect to a "zero line segment." Thus, the figures ABC and $ABFE$ pictured in Fig. 7 are S-equidecomposable.

LEMMA 3*a*. *Two parallelograms of equal area whose bases are equal and parallel are S-equidecomposable.*

By using a parallel translation it is possible to superpose the equal bases of the parallelograms, after which the proof of Lemma 3, section 2 may be applied. In Fig. 9, parts marked by the same numbers are obtained from one another by means of parallel translations.

LEMMA 4*a*. *Two rectangles which have equal areas are S-equidecomposable.*

The proof for Lemma 4, section 2 is not applicable in this case, because it requires a rotation. We must, therefore, give a separate proof for the present lemma.

Let $ABCD$ and $A'B'C'D'$ be two rectangles having equal areas. Construct a parallelogram AB_1C_1D having the same area as these rectangles and having the side AD in common with the rectangle $ABCD$ and the side AB_1 parallel to one of the sides of the rectangle $A'B'C'D'$ (Fig. 27a). Then the parallelograms $ABCD$ and AB_1C_1D

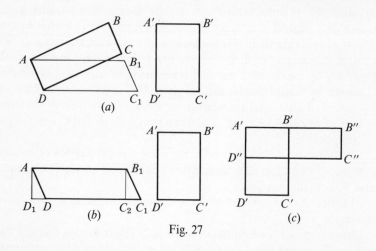

Fig. 27

are S-equidecomposable (Lemma 3a). Now construct the rectangle $AB_1C_2D_1$ equal in area with the original rectangles and having side AB_1 in common with the parallelogram AB_1C_1D (Fig. 27b). Then the figures AB_1C_1D and $AB_1C_2D_1$ are S-equidecomposable. All the corresponding sides of the rectangles $AB_1C_2D_1$ and $A'B'C'D'$ are parallel to one another. Finally, by means of a parallel translation, superimpose the rectangle $AB_1C_2D_1$ upon $A'B'C'D'$ in such a way that the point A coincides with A' and the side AD_1 lies along the side $A'D'$. (This may involve interchanging the names of D' and B'.) We thus obtain the rectangle $A'B''C''D''$, which has the angle A' in common with the rectangle $A'B'C'D'$ (Fig. 27c). Since, in carrying out this construction, we proceed in each case from one parallelogram to another which is S-equidecomposable with it, we see, by Lemma 1a, that we obtain a rectangle $A'B''C''D''$ which is S-equidecomposable with the original rectangle $ABCD$. It remains to be shown that the rectangle $A'B''C''D''$ is S-equidecomposable with the rectangle $A'B'C'D'$. For the sake of argument let us assume that $A'B'' > A'B'$ (so that $A'D'' < A'D'$). Draw the line segments

$B''D'$, $B'D''$, $C''C'$ (Fig. 28); we shall show that these line segments are parallel to one another. From the equality of the areas of

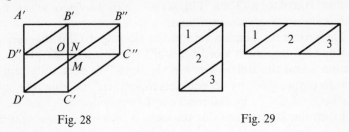

Fig. 28   Fig. 29

the figures in question, we obtain

$$A'B' \cdot A'D' = A'B'' \cdot A'D'', \tag{1}$$

from which, by subtracting the product $A'D'' \cdot A'B'$ from both sides of the equality, we obtain

$$A'B' \cdot D'D'' = A'D'' \cdot B'B'',$$

or

$$A'B' \cdot OC' = A'D'' \cdot OC'', \tag{2}$$

where O is the point of intersection of the lines $B'C'$ and $D''C''$. By writing equalities (1) and (2) as proportions, we obtain

$$\frac{A'B'}{A'D''} = \frac{A'B''}{A'D'} = \frac{OC''}{OC'}.$$

Thus, the right triangles $A'B'D''$, $A'B''D'$, and $OC''C'$ are similar. It follows that $\angle A'D''B' = \angle A'D'B'' = \angle B'C'C''$, and the line segments $B''D'$, $B'D''$, $C'C''$ are, therefore, parallel to one another.

Let M and N be the points of intersection of the line $B''D'$ with the lines $B'C'$ and $C''D''$. Then $\triangle B''C''N \cong \triangle MC'D'$ ($B''C'' = MC'$ and $C''N = C'D'$, since $B''C''C'M$ and $NC''C'D'$ are parallelograms). Furthermore, the parallelograms $B'B''ND''$ and $B'MD'D''$ have equal areas and have a common base $B'D''$, so that by Lemma 3a they are S-equidecomposable. Finally, the triangle $A'B'D''$ is part of both rectangles $A'B'C'D'$ and $A'B''C''D''$. Thus, from the decomposition of each of these rectangles into three parts (Fig. 29) we conclude that they are S-equidecomposable. (The corresponding parts marked "1" and "3" are congruent and are obtained from one another by means of a parallel translation; the parallelograms marked "2" are S-equidecomposable.)

LEMMA 5a. *Every polygon is S-equidecomposable with some rectangle.*

THE HADWIGER-GLUR THEOREM.[1] *Two polygons which have equal areas are S-equidecomposable.*

The proofs for Lemma 5a and the Hadwiger-Glur theorem are obtained by an almost word-for-word repetition of the proofs for Lemma 5 and the Bolyai-Gerwin theorem. We need only replace "equidecomposable" by "S-equidecomposable," and the references to Lemmas 1, 2, . . . by references to Lemmas 1a, 2a, ...

From the Hadwiger-Glur theorem it follows at once that two polygons having equal areas can be decomposed into parts so that the corresponding sides of pairs of congruent parts are parallel. For if A and B are polygons which have equal areas, it is possible to decompose one of them into parts which may be rearranged to give the other polygon by using parallel translations and central symmetries alone. It remains to note that if two polygons are obtained from each other by means of a parallel translation (Fig. 21) or a central symmetry (Fig. 22), their corresponding sides will be parallel.

---

[1] See [2] in the Bibliography.

3. Equidecomposability and the Concept of Additive Invariants

Having proved the Hadwiger-Glur theorem, we next turn to the related question: is it possible to decompose polygons having equal areas into parts which may be obtained from one another by means of *parallel translations alone?* In other words, is the application of central symmetries in the preceding section superfluous? The present chapter is devoted to consideration of this question. We shall see that not every pair of polygons of equal area can be decomposed into parts obtainable from one another by means of parallel translations alone; in particular, a triangle and a parallelogram having the same area do not admit of such a decomposition.

In order to establish these results, we shall make use of the concept of an *additive invariant*, which is defined below. This concept is also employed in later sections.

6. THE ADDITIVE INVARIANT $J_l(M)$

Let M be an arbitrary polygon, each of whose sides is marked with an arrow pointing in such a way that by proceeding along this side in the direction of the arrow the points to our left belong to the polygon, while the points to our right do not belong to it (Fig. 30).[1]

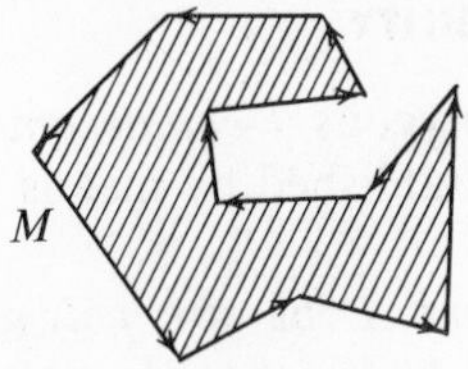

Fig. 30

[1] If we move along the sides of the polygon one by one, moving in the direction indicated by the arrows, we shall describe a complete circuit around the polygon and return to the starting point. In this case we say that we have completed a circuit of the polygon moving counterclockwise.

Choose an arbitrary oriented straight line l, that is, a straight line whose direction is indicated by an arrow. Let us denote by $J_l(M)$ the algebraic sum of the lengths of all the sides of the polygon M parallel to the straight line l, taking the lengths of those sides which have the *same* direction as the straight line l (the sides AB, DE, and FG in Fig. 31) to be positive, and the lengths of those

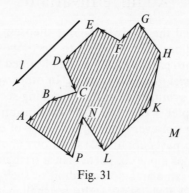

Fig. 31

which have the *opposite* direction (the side KL in Fig. 31) to be negative. If no side of the polygon M is parallel to the straight line l, then $J_l(M)$ is taken to be the number zero. The number $J_l(M)$ is called an *additive invariant*. (The reason for choosing this terminology is given below.)

The importance of the invariant $J_l(M)$ for the problem of the equidecomposability of polygons will be evident from the theorem which we shall now formulate.

7. *T-EQUIDECOMPOSABILITY*

We shall call two polygons *T-equidecomposable* if their equidecomposability can be established by means of parallel translations alone.

THEOREM. *Let A and A' be two polygons, and l an oriented straight line. If $J_l(A) \neq J_l(A')$, then the polygons A and A' are not T-equidecomposable.*

The proof for this theorem will be given below, but first we shall note one simple result which follows from it. Let Δ be a triangle and P a parallelogram of the same area (the base of the parallelogram is taken to be parallel to the base of the triangle (Fig. 32)). Choose a straight line l parallel to the base of the triangle and

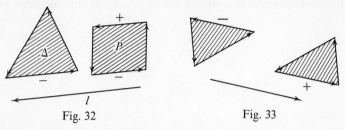

Fig. 32   Fig. 33

the base of the parallelogram, and fix the signs on the sides in accordance with the rule given above (Fig. 32). We then find that $J_l(P) = 0$, $J_l(\Delta) \neq 0$, so that $J_l(P) \neq J_l(\Delta)$; therefore, the figures P and Δ are not T-equidecomposable. The congruent triangles in Fig. 33 are not T-equidecomposable either.

We now proceed to the proof of the theorem stated above.

8. PROPERTIES OF THE INVARIANT $J_l(M)$

LEMMA 10. *Let l be an oriented straight line, and M and M' two polygons obtained from each other by means of a parallel translation; then $J_l(M) = J_l(M')$.*

In other words, the number J_l remains unchanged for polygons which are subjected to a parallel translation; it is for this reason that the term *invariant* is used for J_l. (It does not vary under translation.)

The proof for this lemma is self-evident. For, when a polygon undergoes parallel translation, the lengths and directions of its sides do not undergo any change.

LEMMA 11. *Let l be an oriented straight line, and A some polygon decomposed into a finite number of polygons $M_1, M_2, \ldots, M_k$. Then*

$$J_l(A) = J_l(M_1) + J_l(M_2) + \cdots + J_l(M_k). \qquad (3)$$

In other words, if the polygon A consists of several smaller polygons, then $J_l(A)$ may be obtained by the addition of the invariants of the constituent polygons, whence the name *additive* invariant.

Proof. Let us examine all the line segments which are sides of the polygons $A, M_1, M_2, \ldots, M_k$. On these line segments mark all

23

those points which are vertices of the polygons A, M_1, M_2, ..., M_k. We thus obtain a finite number of (possibly shorter) line segments, which we shall call *links*. Fig. 34 shows the decomposition

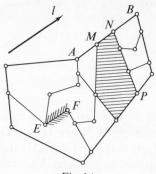

Fig. 34

of a polygon into smaller polygons. The side AB consists of three links: AM, MN, NB; the side NP, which in the illustration is a side of the shaded polygon, also consists of three links.

Note that in calculating the invariant $J_l(A)$ of the polygon A (or of any one of the polygons M_1, M_2, ..., M_k) we may take the algebraic sum of the links parallel to the straight line l instead of the algebraic sum of the sides, since the length of each side is equal to the sum of the lengths of the links of which it is composed. Therefore, in order to calculate the sum appearing on the right in equation (3), we must calculate the algebraic sum of the lengths of all the links parallel to the straight line l, taking into account the links for each of the polygons M_1, M_2, ..., M_k.

Let us examine a link which lies completely *within* the polygon A (except perhaps for its end points): the link EF in Fig. 34. There will be *two* of the polygons M_1, M_2, ..., M_k which border on the link in question, lying on opposite sides of it (one on the right, the other on the left). In the calculation of the invariant of one of these polygons, the link in question will have one sign, but in the calculation of the invariant for the other polygon, it will have the opposite sign; thus, in the algebraic sum of all the links, these two terms will cancel each other. We thus see that in calculating the right-hand side of (3), it is possible to neglect those links which lie completely *within* the polygon A.

Let us now consider some link which lies on the perimeter of the polygon A and which is parallel to the straight line l (the link AM in Fig. 34). Only one of the polygons M_1, M_2, ..., M_k borders on this link, and it lies on the same side of the link as does the polygon A. Consequently, this link enters into the sum $J_l(M_1) + J_l(M_2) + \cdots + J_l(M_k)$ with the same sign as it does in the sum which gives the invariant $J_l(A)$. Thus, the right-hand side of equality (3) is equal to $J_l(A)$; that is, equality (3) has been verified.

Now we can readily proceed to the proof of the theorem stated in section 7. Suppose the polygons A and A' are T-equidecomposable. This means that A is made up of polygons M_1, M_2, ..., M_k and A' of polygons M_1', M_2', ..., M_k' such that M_1 and M_1' are obtainable from each other by means of a parallel translation, the same being true for M_2 and M_2', etc. Then in accordance with Lemma 10 we have

$$J_l(M_1) = J_l(M_1'), \ J_l(M_2) = J_l(M_2'), \ \ldots, \ J_l(M_k) = J_l(M_k'); \quad (4)$$

and according to Lemma 11,

$$\left. \begin{array}{l} J_l(A) = J_l(M_l) + J_l(M_2) + \cdots + J_l(M_k), \\ J_l(A') = J_l(M_1') + J_l(M_2') + \cdots + J_l(M_k'). \end{array} \right\} \quad (5)$$

From (4) and (5) it follows that $J_l(A) = J_l(A')$. Thus, it is seen that if the inequality $J_l(A) \neq J_l(A')$ holds, the polygons A and A' cannot be T-equidecomposable.

9. CENTRALLY SYMMETRIC POLYGONS

The theorem whose proof is given above may also be stated as follows: two polygons A and A' are T-equidecomposable only if the equality $J_l(A) = J_l(A')$ holds for every straight line l. In other words, in order that the polygons A and A' be T-equidecomposable, it is *necessary* that $J_l(A) = J_l(A')$. It can be shown that this condition is also *sufficient*, that is, that the following proposition holds.

THEOREM. *If two polygons A and A' having equal areas are such that the equality $J_l(A) = J_l(A')$ holds for every oriented straight line l, the polygons A and A' are T-equidecomposable* (see [2]).

We now pose the following problem: find all *convex* polygons which are T-equidecomposable with a square. It is easily seen that for a square Q the invariant $J_l(Q)$ is zero, regardless of what straight line l we may choose. (The case for which l is parallel to one of the sides of the square is represented in Fig. 35.) Our problem may,

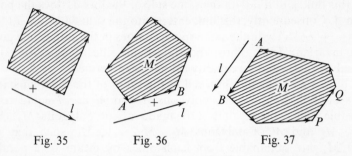

Fig. 35   Fig. 36   Fig. 37

therefore, be formulated as follows: find all convex polygons whose invariant J_l is equal to zero for every oriented straight line l. Let M be a polygon having this property, AB one of its sides, and l a straight line parallel to AB. Then the polygon M must have another side parallel to AB (since otherwise $J_l(M) \neq 0$, being equal to $+$ or $-$ the length of AB; see Fig. 36). Denoting the side which is parallel to AB by PQ,[1] we have $J_l(M) = \pm$ [length (AB) − length (PQ)]; and since $J_l(M)$ must be zero, we have $AB = PQ$. Thus, for each side of the polygon M there is a side of the polygon equal in length and parallel to it (but oriented in the opposite direction). It follows that the polygon M is symmetric about a point. It is clear that the converse also holds: if the polygon M is symmetric about a point, the invariant $J_l(M)$ for any arbitrary straight line l must be zero. Thus, *for a convex polygon to be T-equidecomposable with a square, it is necessary and sufficient that this polygon be symmetric about a point.*

We obtained this result by using the formulation (but not the proof) of the theorem stated above. By referring to Fig. 38, how-

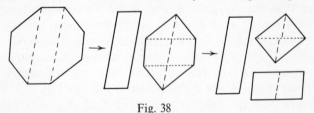

Fig. 38

[1] Since the polygon M is convex, it cannot have more than two sides parallel to the straight line l.

ever, the reader can readily prove for himself (without having recourse to this theorem) that a polygon which is symmetric about a point can be transformed into a series of parallelograms (by decomposing it into parts and applying to each part a parallel translation), and then into a square (see the proof of Lemma 3).

4. Equidecomposability and the Concept of Groups

10. GROUPS

In Chapter 2 we dealt with the *motions* of a plane. Let us denote by D the set of all motions of a given plane; the individual motions will be referred to as the *elements* of this *set D*. For instance, each parallel translation (as well as each central symmetry) is an element of the set D. The product of any pair of motions is defined; that is, the set D has the following property:

PROPERTY 1. *For every pair of elements d_1, d_2 of the set D the product $d_1 \cdot d_2$ is defined and is also an element of the set D.*

Among these motions there is one which plays a special role. This is the motion which leaves the whole figure in its original position, a motion which is, so to speak, "the zero motion." We shall denote this motion by the letter e and call it the *identity* motion. It is characterized by the property that each of the products $d \cdot e$ and $e \cdot d$ is identical with d, for any motion d:

$$d \cdot e = e \cdot d = d.$$

For if the figure in question first undergoes the motion e (as a result of which it remains in its original position), and then the motion d, the result is the same as if it had undergone only the motion d, that is, $e \cdot d = d$. It is equally clear that $d \cdot e = d$. This property of the motion e recalls the property of the number 1 in multiplication ($a \cdot 1 = 1 \cdot a = a$, for an arbitrary number a). In view of this analogy, the motion e is also called *unity*.

PROPERTY 2. *The set D contains an element e, called the identity element, for which the equality*

$$d \cdot e = e \cdot d = d \tag{6}$$

holds for every element of D.

Furthermore, for each motion d there exists an *inverse* motion, which we denote by d^{-1}. The product of the motion d and its inverse motion d^{-1} (as well as the product of the motion d^{-1} and the motion d) is a motion which has the effect of leaving the whole figure in its original position. Thus, we have

$$d \cdot d^{-1} = d^{-1} \cdot d = e.$$

We incorporate this result in the following:

PROPERTY 3. *For each element d of the set D there is a corresponding element d^{-1}, also belonging to the set D, and called the inverse of the element d, for which the following equality holds:*

$$d \cdot d^{-1} = d^{-1} \cdot d = e. \tag{7}$$

Let d_1, d_2, and d_3 be three motions. Assume that some figure A undergoes the motion d_1 which converts it to the figure B; then figure B is transformed into the figure C by the motion d_2; and finally the figure C is transformed into the figure D by the motion d_3. Let us examine the product $(d_1 \cdot d_2) \cdot d_3$ obtained by multiplying d_1 by d_2 and next multiplying this product by d_3. The motion $d_1 \cdot d_2$ converts the figure A into the figure C as one may readily see; then the motion d_3 transforms the figure C into the figure D. Therefore, the motion $(d_1 \cdot d_2) \cdot d_3$ has the net effect of transforming the figure A into the figure D. By taking the product of the three motions in a different order, $d_1 \cdot (d_2 \cdot d_3)$, we find that figure A is transformed by the motion d_1 into the figure B, which is then transformed into the figure D by the motion $d_2 \cdot d_3$. Thus, both motions $(d_1 \cdot d_2) \cdot d_3$ and $d_1 \cdot (d_2 \cdot d_3)$ transform the figure A into the same figure; that is, these motions are identical. Thus, we have

PROPERTY 4. *For any three elements d_1, d_2, d_3 of the set D, the equation*

$$(d_1 \cdot d_2) \cdot d_3 = d_1 \cdot (d_2 \cdot d_3) \tag{8}$$

holds. This property is known as associativity.

Thus, the set D of all motions possesses Properties 1–4 listed above. A set consisting of an arbitrary collection of elements for which a product is defined satisfying 1–4 is called a *group*.[1]

---

[1] We shall examine here only groups of motions (see below). As an example of a group whose elements are not motions we may cite the set G of *all positive numbers*, the product operation being ordinary multiplication (the number 1 is the identity of this group; the inverse of the number a is the number $\frac{1}{a} = a^{-1}$). Many more examples of groups could be given.

The group concept plays an important role in modern mathematics. The interested reader may be referred to the book *An Introduction to the Theory of Groups* by P. S. Alexandroff (New York: Hafner Publishing Company, 1959). This book is written from an elementary point of view and contains many very interesting examples. We note that Alexandroff calls the group operation *addition* instead of multiplication.

11. GROUPS OF MOTIONS

As we have seen, the set D of all motions of the plane constitutes a group. Let us now examine the set S consisting of all parallel translations and central symmetries and show that this set is also a group. Indeed, the elements of the set S are motions; for each pair of these (as also for pairs of arbitrary motions) the *product* is defined and is by Lemma 9 again an element of the set S. Thus, Property 1 is fulfilled. It is clear that Property 2 is also fulfilled, since the motion e is a parallel translation and hence belongs to the set S. Moreover, equation (6) holds for motions in general and hence, in particular, for parallel translations and central symmetries, that is, for elements of the set S. Property 3 is fulfilled, because the inverse of a parallel translation is a parallel translation, and the inverse of a central symmetry is a central symmetry (Lemma 6); from this it follows that equality (7), which holds for all motions, holds in particular for the elements of the set S. Finally, the associative law (8), which holds for *all* motions, holds also for translations and central symmetries. Thus, the set S is a group.

Quite analogously it may be shown that the set T of *all parallel translations* constitutes a group.

A set G is called a *group of motions* if its elements are motions, if it is clear in just what sense its elements are to be multiplied, and if the elements fulfill the Properties 1–4. As examples of groups of motions we may cite the groups D, S, and T examined above. Still another example of a group of motions is the group Z_n, consisting of rotations about a fixed point through one of the angles 0, $\dfrac{2\pi}{n}$, $\dfrac{4\pi}{n}$, $\dfrac{6\pi}{n}$, ..., $\dfrac{(2n-2)\pi}{n}$, n an integer. (The rotation through the angle 0 is the identity motion e.) We leave it to the reader to verify that Z_n is a group. We remark only that, as this example shows, a group may consist of a finite number of elements (the group Z_n contains n elements).

Let G be a group of motions, and let A and A' be two polygons. Assume that we can decompose the polygon A into parts M_1, M_2, ..., M_k, and the polygon A' into parts M_1', M_2', ..., M_k', so that corresponding parts can be obtained from one another by means of motions belonging to the group G (that is, the group G contains a motion g_1 which transforms the polygon M_1 into M_1', a motion g_2 which transforms M_2 into M_2', and so on). In this case the polygons A and A' are called G-*equidecomposable*. If the group G hap-

30

pens to be one of the groups S or T, we have the concepts of S- or T-equidecomposability examined above. All pairs of polygons of equal area are D-equidecomposable (Bolyai-Gerwin theorem) and even S-equidecomposable (Hadwiger-Glur theorem), but not all pairs of polygons of equal area are T-equidecomposable (for example, a triangle and a parallelogram are not).

12. A PROPERTY OF THE GROUP S (OPTIONAL)

We state the following theorem in answer to a question which may have occurred to the reader:

THEOREM. *The group S is the smallest group of motions which enables one to establish the equidecomposability of arbitrary pairs of polygons having equal areas. In other words, if G is a group of motions such that any two polygons whatever having equal areas are G-equidecomposable, the group G will contain the whole group S (that is, will contain all parallel translations and central symmetries).*

Proof. The proof is based on several lemmas; in formulating these lemmas we shall assume that G is a group which satisfies the conditions of the theorem.

LEMMA 12. *If P and Q are arbitrary points of the plane, the group G will contain a motion which transforms P into Q* (this property of a group of motions is called transitivity).

Let us assume otherwise; that is, let us assume that there exist two points P and Q such that no motion belonging to the group G transforms P into Q. Let us call the set of all points of the plane into which P can be transformed by motions belonging to the group G the *orbit* of P. Let M be a polygon; denote the sum of all angles of M whose vertices lie in the orbit of P by $I_P(M)$. If the polygons M and M' can be obtained from one another by some motion belonging to the group G, then $I_P(M) = I_P(M')$. Moreover, if a polygon A is decomposed into a number of smaller polygons M_1, M_2, $\ldots$, M_k, then the equality

$$I_P(A) = I_P(M_1) + I_P(M_2) + \cdots + I_P(M_k) + n\pi$$

will hold, where n is an integer. (This follows directly from the calculation of the angles.) From these properties of the number $I_P(M)$ it follows readily (see arguments in section 8) that if A and A' are two G-equidecomposable polygons, then $I_P(A) = I_P(A') + n\pi$, where n is some integer.

31

Now let PQR and PQS be two congruent obtuse isosceles triangles with base angle α, the obtuse angle of PQR being at P and of PQS being at Q (Fig. 39). Since the point P is in the orbit of P while Q is not, the number $I_P(PQR)$ is equal to $\pi - \alpha$ or $\pi - 2\alpha$ (depending on whether the point R is or is not in the orbit of P); the number $I_P(PQS)$ is equal to α or 2α. Therefore, the equality

$$I_P(PQR) = I_P(PQS) + n\pi$$

cannot hold for any integer n (since $\alpha < \dfrac{\pi}{4}$), and the triangles PQR and PQS are not G-equidecomposable. This, however, contradicts the properties of the group G (polygons which are equal in area and, all the more, polygons which are congruent must be G-equidecomposable). Thus, the lemma is proved by contradiction.

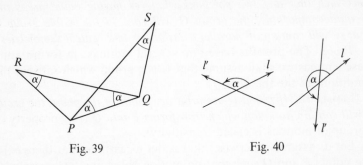

Fig. 39   Fig. 40

LEMMA 13. *The group G contains at least one central symmetry.*
We note first of all (without proof[1]) some properties of motions. Every motion of a plane is of one of the following three types: it is either a parallel translation, a rotation, or a so-called *sliding symmetry*, which is a symmetry relative to some straight line[2] accompanied by a parallel translation along this straight line. This straight line is called the *axis* of the sliding symmetry. The axis is uniquely

[1] The proofs of these properties of motions may be found in the book by O. Schreier and E. Sperner, *Modern Algebra and Matrix Theory* (New York: Chelsea Publishing Company, 1959), pp. 162–168.

[2] Let us recall the definition of a symmetry with respect to a straight line. Let l be a straight line. If AA' is a line segment which is perpendicular to the line l and whose mid-point lies on the line l, its end points A and A' are said to be *symmetric* with respect to the line l. If every point of a figure F is transformed into the point symmetric to it (with respect to l), a new figure F' is obtained. We say that F and F' are *symmetric* to one another with respect to the line l.

defined; that is, two sliding symmetries whose axes do not coincide are *distinct* motions. Finally, we note that the product of two sliding symmetries whose axes form an angle α with one another is a *rotation* through an angle 2α. We shall use these properties in the proof of Lemma 13.

Let us now proceed to the proof of Lemma 13. Choose a straight line l as follows: if the group G contains at least one sliding symmetry, let us take its axis to be the line l; otherwise take l to be an arbitrary straight line. The line l is given either of its two orientations. Let l' be an arbitrary oriented straight line, and let α be the angle between l and l' (Fig. 40); then the straight line l' is said to lie in the *orbit* of l provided the group G includes a rotation through the angle α. In particular, every straight line parallel to l (that is, forming a zero angle with l) is in the orbit of l.

Let us assume (in contradiction to Lemma 13) that the group G does not contain a single central symmetry. Then for any straight line l' in the orbit of l, a straight line l'' which is parallel to l' but having the opposite direction is not in the orbit of l (otherwise the group G would contain two rotations whose angles differ by π and, therefore, would also contain a rotation through the angle π, that is, a central symmetry; see Fig. 41).

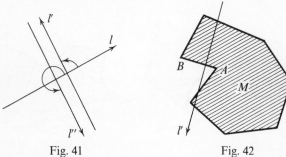

Fig. 41   Fig. 42

Let us consider an arbitrary polygon M, and let AB be a side of M, and l' a line intersecting this side and perpendicular to it. The straight line l' is oriented in such a way that by proceeding along its positive direction we shall move from the interior of the polygon M to the exterior upon crossing the side AB (Fig. 42). If the straight line l' oriented in this manner is in the orbit of l, the side AB is given a positive sign; if the straight line l'' parallel to l' but oriented in the opposite direction is in the orbit of l, this side is given a negative sign; finally, if neither of these conditions holds, the side AB is assigned the value zero. Let us now compute the algebraic sum of the lengths of the sides of the polygon M, taking into account the indicated signs. (If the side AB is assigned the value zero, it has no effect upon this algebraic sum.) Let us call the algebraic sum obtained $J'_l(M)$.

The number $J'_l(M)$ has the following two properties: (1) it is *additive* (see formula (3)), and (2) it is *invariant* (if the polygons M_1 and M_2 can be obtained from one another by means of some motion belonging to the group G, then $J'_l(M_1) = J'_l(M_2)$).

Additivity can be proved by an almost verbatim repetition of the proof for Lemma 11.

Let us show that $J'_l(M)$ is invariant. Let g be a motion belonging to the group G which converts the polygon M_1 into the polygon M_2; let A_1B_1 be a side of the polygon M_1, and A_2B_2 the side of the polygon M_2 corresponding to it (that is, the side into which A_1B_1 is transformed by the motion g). Further, let l_1 be a straight line perpendicular to the side A_1B_1, and let l_2 be a straight line perpendicular to A_2B_2, each of these lines being oriented in such a way as to proceed from the interior to the exterior of the corresponding polygon at the point of intersection of the side in question (Fig. 43).

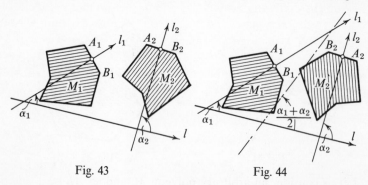

Fig. 43   Fig. 44

The angles formed by the straight lines l_1 and l_2 with the straight line l we denote by α_1 and α_2, respectively. Let us assume that the straight line l_1 is in the orbit of l. We shall show that l_2 is also in the orbit of l. (1) If the motion g is a parallel translation, the line l_2 is parallel to the line l_1, has the same direction, and therefore is in the orbit of l. (2) If g is a rotation, the angle of this rotation is $\alpha_2 - \alpha_1$. But since G contains a rotation through the angle α_1 (the straight line l_1 is in the orbit of l), G must also contain a rotation through the angle $(\alpha_2 - \alpha_1) + \alpha_1 = \alpha_2$; this implies that the straight line l_2 is in the orbit of l. If g is a sliding symmetry, the axis of the symmetry forms an angle $\dfrac{\alpha_1 + \alpha_2}{2}$ with the straight line l, which is in this case also the axis of a sliding symmetry, by our initial choice for l (Fig. 44). Therefore, the group G contains a rotation through the angle $\alpha_1 + \alpha_2$. Furthermore, since G contains a rotation through the angle α_1 (as remarked above), it also contains a rotation through the angle $(\alpha_1 + \alpha_2) - \alpha_1 = \alpha_2$. Thus, also in this case the straight line l_2 is in the orbit of l. To summarize, then, if the side A_1B_1 of the polygon M_1 is of positive sign (that is, if the straight line l_1 is in the orbit of l), the side A_2B_2 of the polygon M_2 is also of positive sign. Analogously, one can show that if the side A_1B_1 is of negative sign, the side A_2B_2 is of negative sign. Finally, if the side A_1B_1 has the value zero, so does the side A_2B_2 (the polygon M_1 is obtained from M_2 by means of the motion g^{-1}, and if the sign of the side A_2B_2 were either positive or negative, the side A_1B_1 would be of the same sign). Thus, the corresponding sides of the polygons M_1 and M_2 are included in the algebraic sums $J_l'(M_1)$ and $J_l'(M_2)$ with identical coefficients, so that $J_l'(M_1) = J_l'(M_2)$.

From the additivity and invariance of the number $J_l'(M)$ it follows that (see sections 8 and 9) if the polygons M_1 and M_2 are G-equidecomposable, then $J_l'(M_1) = J_l'(M_2)$.

Let us now examine two congruent isosceles right triangles $A_1B_1C_1$ and $A_2B_2C_2$ situated as indicated in Fig. 45. The side B_2C_2 of the triangle $A_2B_2C_2$ has the value zero, since the straight line l' which is perpendicular to this side forms the angle $\dfrac{3}{4}\pi$ with l and a rotation through $\dfrac{3}{4}\pi$ is not in the group G (since four applications of this rotation are equivalent to a rotation through the angle 3π, that

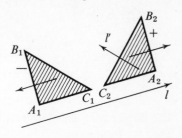

Fig. 45

is, a central symmetry). Analogously, to each of the sides A_1C_1, B_1C_1, and A_2C_2 corresponds the number zero. Finally, side A_2B_2 has a positive sign, whereas the sign of the side A_1B_1 is negative. We see that $J_l'(A_1B_1C_1) \neq J_l'(A_2B_2C_2)$ (since one of these numbers is positive, while the other is negative), from which it follows that the triangles $A_1B_1C_1$ and $A_2B_2C_2$ are not G-equidecomposable. This, however, contradicts the properties of the group G.

LEMMA 14. *The group G contains all central symmetries.*

Let s be a central symmetry belonging to the group G (Lemma 13), O_1 the center of this symmetry, and O an arbitrary point of the plane. Further, let g be a motion belonging to the group G which transforms the point O into the point O_1 (Lemma 12). It is easy to see that the motion gsg^{-1}, which belongs to the group G, leaves the point O in its original position and constitutes the central symmetry with respect to the point O. Thus, the central symmetry with respect to the point O belongs to the group G.

For the proof of the theorem it remains only to note that in accordance with Lemma 7 the group G also contains all parallel translations.

5. The Theorems of Dehn and Hadwiger
for Polyhedra

13. EQUIDECOMPOSABLE POLYHEDRA

We shall now begin to examine the problems of equidecomposability and equicomplementability for solid bodies (polyhedra). Two polyhedra are said to be equidecomposable if one of them can be decomposed into a finite number of parts in such a way that these parts may be rearranged to form the other one.

It is clear that two equidecomposable polyhedra have equal volumes. Of course, the question arises as to whether the converse holds: are all pairs of polyhedra which have equal volumes necessarily equidecomposable? In other words, is there a theorem which applies to polyhedra which is analogous to that of Bolyai and Gerwin? We shall see presently that this question must be answered in the negative.

First of all we shall examine the significance of a negative answer to this question. Does such an answer mean that there are no two polyhedra of equal volume which are equidecomposable? Naturally this is not the case. It is obvious that there do exist equidecomposable polyhedra. For instance, two right prisms having equal altitudes and bases of equal area are equidecomposable (Fig. 46). This follows at once from the Bolyai-Gerwin theorem. (We

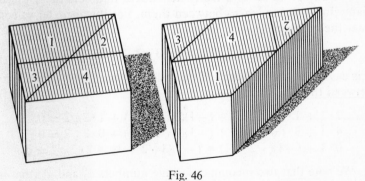

Fig. 46

shall prove below (section 19) that any two prisms having equal volumes, whether they be right prisms or oblique, are equidecomposable.) What then does a negative answer to the above question mean? It means that *not all* polyhedra having the same volume are equidecomposable. In other words, while some polyhedra having equal volumes are in fact equidecomposable (for example, prisms), *there also exist polyhedra which are equal in volume but are not equidecomposable.* This was first proved by the German mathematician Dehn in [1]. He showed that a cube and a regular triangular pyramid (tetrahedron) which have equal volumes are not equidecomposable. Of course, there exist other polyhedra which have equal volumes and are not equidecomposable.

In this chapter we present a proof for the theorem of Dehn which asserts the nonequidecomposability of a cube with a regular tetrahedron. The proof makes use of some clever ideas of the Swiss mathematician Hadwiger.

14. THE THEOREM OF HADWIGER

Let $\alpha_1, \alpha_2, \ldots, \alpha_k$ be arbitrary real numbers. We shall say that these numbers are *linearly dependent* in case there exist integers $n_1, n_2, \ldots, n_k$, not all zero, such that

$$n_1\alpha_1 + n_2\alpha_2 + \cdots + n_k\alpha_k = 0. \tag{9}$$

We shall call an equation such as (9) a *linear dependence* between the numbers $\alpha_1, \alpha_2, \ldots, \alpha_k$. We must stress that all the numbers $n_1, n_2, \ldots, n_k$ are assumed to be integers (positive, negative, or zero), at least one of them being different from zero.

For any given set of linearly dependent numbers there will be many linear dependences between them. For instance, let us consider the numbers

$$\alpha_1 = 1, \ \alpha_2 = \sqrt{2} - 1, \ \alpha_3 = 3\sqrt{2} + 1, \ \alpha_4 = 2\sqrt{2}.$$

It is easy to verify that each of the following is a linear dependence between these numbers:

$$2 \cdot 1 + 1 \cdot (\sqrt{2} - 1) + (-1)(3\sqrt{2} + 1) + 1 \cdot 2\sqrt{2} = 0,$$
$$4 \cdot 1 + 3 \cdot (\sqrt{2} - 1) + (-1)(3\sqrt{2} + 1) + 0 \cdot 2\sqrt{2} = 0,$$
$$0 \cdot 1 + (-1)(\sqrt{2} - 1) + (-1)(3\sqrt{2} + 1) + 2 \cdot 2\sqrt{2} = 0.$$

We note that two incommensurable numbers α_1 and α_2 (that is, two numbers which are different from zero and whose quotient is irrational) cannot be linearly dependent. Indeed, the linear dependence

$$n_1\alpha_1 + n_2\alpha_2 = 0$$

shows that the quotient $\frac{\alpha_1}{\alpha_2}$ ($\alpha_2 \neq 0$) is equal to the quotient $-\frac{n_2}{n_1}$ of two integers, that is, is rational.

Let us now assume that there is some rule for assigning to each of the numbers $\alpha_1, \alpha_2, \ldots, \alpha_k$ another number corresponding to it:

to α_1 a corresponding number $f(\alpha_1)$,
to α_2 a corresponding number $f(\alpha_2)$,
. . . .
to α_k a corresponding number $f(\alpha_k)$.

We shall say that the numbers $f(\alpha_1), f(\alpha_2), \ldots, f(\alpha_k)$ define an *additive function* of the numbers[1] $\alpha_1, \alpha_2, \ldots, \alpha_k$ provided they have the following property: for each linear dependence

$$n_1\alpha_1 + n_2\alpha_2 + \cdots + n_k\alpha_k = 0$$

between the numbers $\alpha_1, \alpha_2, \ldots, \alpha_k$, the analogous equation

$$n_1f(\alpha_1) + n_2f(\alpha_2) + \cdots + n_kf(\alpha_k) = 0$$

is a linear dependence between the numbers $f(\alpha_1), f(\alpha_2), \ldots, f(\alpha_k)$.

If the numbers $\alpha_1, \alpha_2, \ldots, \alpha_k$ are not linearly dependent in the first place, then the numbers $f(\alpha_1), f(\alpha_2), \ldots, f(\alpha_k)$ may be chosen in an arbitrary manner. For instance, let us consider the numbers $\alpha_1 = 1$, $\alpha_2 = \sqrt{5}$. Since these numbers are incommensurable, there is no linear dependence between them. Consequently, when it comes to specifying the numbers $f(\alpha_1)$ and $f(\alpha_2)$ corresponding to α_1 and α_2, there is no need to require that the numbers to be specified be linearly dependent. In other words, we shall obtain an additive function of $\alpha_1 = 1$ and $\alpha_2 = \sqrt{5}$ no matter what values we choose for $f(1)$ and $f(\sqrt{5})$. In case the numbers $\alpha_1, \alpha_2, \ldots, \alpha_k$ are linearly

---

[1] According to the modern point of view, a function is defined if to each element of a set there corresponds (by some rule) a definite element of another set. Thus, if to each real number x we assign as a corresponding number the number $\sin x$, we obtain a function (the sine function); if to each number in the set of positive integers we assign as a corresponding number the greatest prime divisor of that positive integer, we obtain a function. In general, by setting up a correspondence between the numbers α_1, $\alpha_2, \ldots, \alpha_k$ and some other numbers $f(\alpha_1), f(\alpha_2), \ldots, f(\alpha_k)$, we shall obtain a function f.

dependent, it follows from our definition of an additive function that for any additive function f the corresponding numbers $f(\alpha_1)$, $f(\alpha_2), \ldots, f(\alpha_k)$ will also be linearly dependent.

Finally, let

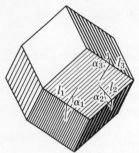

Fig. 47

$$\alpha_1, \alpha_2, \ldots, \alpha_k \tag{10}$$

be the internal dihedral angles, expressed in radians, of some polyhedron A, and let $l_1, l_2, \ldots, l_k$ be the lengths of the edges corresponding to these dihedral angles (Fig. 47). If an additive function

$$f(\alpha_1), f(\alpha_2), \ldots, f(\alpha_k) \tag{11}$$

is chosen for the numbers (10), then we define

$$f(A) = l_1 f(\alpha_1) + l_2 f(\alpha_2) + \cdots + l_k f(\alpha_k), \tag{12}$$

and we shall call $f(A)$ an *invariant* of the polyhedron A. The invariant $f(A)$ depends not only on the choice of the polyhedron A, but also on the choice of the additive function (11).

We are now in a position to formulate the following interesting theorem.

THE THEOREM OF HADWIGER. *Given two polyhedra A and B of equal volume, we denote by $\alpha_1, \alpha_2, \ldots, \alpha_p$ all the different internal dihedral angles (expressed in radians) of the polyhedron A, and by $\beta_1, \beta_2, \ldots, \beta_q$ all the different internal dihedral angles of the polyhedron B. To the set of numbers $\alpha_1, \alpha_2, \ldots, \alpha_p, \beta_1, \beta_2, \ldots, \beta_q$ we adjoin the number π. If for the set of numbers thus obtained,*

$$\pi, \alpha_1, \alpha_2, \ldots, \alpha_p, \beta_1, \beta_2, \ldots, \beta_q, \tag{13}$$

there exists an additive function,

$$f(\pi), f(\alpha_1), f(\alpha_2), \ldots, f(\alpha_p), f(\beta_1), f(\beta_2), \ldots, f(\beta_q), \tag{14}$$

such that

$$f(\pi) = 0, \tag{15}$$

and if the corresponding invariants for the polyhedra A and B are not equal,

$$f(A) \neq f(B), \tag{16}$$

then the polyhedra A and B are not equidecomposable.

40

We shall prove this theorem of Hadwiger later (section 16); for the present we shall show how the theorem of Dehn asserting the nonequidecomposability of a cube and a regular tetrahedron follows from it.

15. THE THEOREM OF DEHN

First of all we shall prove the following lemma, by means of which we can easily prove Dehn's theorem (using also the theorem of Hadwiger).

LEMMA 15. *Let n be an integer greater than 2, and φ an angle, expressed in radians, whose cosine is $\frac{1}{n}$ (that is, $\cos^{-1}\frac{1}{n} = \varphi$). Then the numbers φ and π are incommensurable; that is, there is no linear dependence of the form*

$$n_1\varphi + n_2\pi = 0, \tag{17}$$

where each of the coefficients n_1, n_2 is a nonzero integer.

We give an indirect proof. Let us suppose that there is a relationship (17) for which $n_1 \neq 0$. We may assume that $n_1 > 0$ (since we can multiply (17) by -1 if $n_1 < 0$). Since $n_1\varphi = -n_2\pi$ is an integral multiple of π, $\cos n_1\varphi$ is equal to $+1$ or else to -1; that is, it is an integer. We shall show that for any integer $k > 0$, $\cos k\varphi$ must be nonintegral.

Making use of the addition formulas from trigonometry, we can write

$$\cos(k+1)\varphi = \cos(k\varphi + \varphi) = \cos k\varphi \cos\varphi - \sin k\varphi \sin\varphi,$$
$$\cos(k-1)\varphi = \cos(k\varphi - \varphi) = \cos k\varphi \cos\varphi + \sin k\varphi \sin\varphi.$$

Adding these two equalities, we obtain

$$\cos(k+1)\varphi + \cos(k-1)\varphi = 2\cos k\varphi \cos\varphi$$

or

$$\cos(k+1)\varphi = \frac{2}{n}\cos k\varphi - \cos(k-1)\varphi \tag{18}$$

(since $\cos\varphi = \frac{1}{n}$). In order to complete the proof, we consider separately the case in which n is odd and the case in which n is even.

Case 1. The number n is odd.[1] Let us use mathematical induction to show that in this case cos $k\varphi$ can be expressed in the form of a fraction whose denominator is n^k and whose numerator is relatively prime to n. From this it will follow that for $k > 0$, cos $k\varphi$ is not an integer, contrary to what we have said above. For $k = 1$ and $k = 2$ the statement we wish to prove can be verified directly:

$$\cos \varphi = \frac{1}{n},$$

$$\cos 2\varphi = 2\cos^2 \varphi - 1$$

$$= \frac{2}{n^2} - 1 = \frac{2 - n^2}{n^2}.$$

(Since n is odd, the numbers 2 and n are relatively prime.) Let us now assume that our statement is true for each of the numbers 1, 2, ..., k, and let us prove that it must then be true for the number $k + 1$. By the induction hypothesis we have

$$\cos k\varphi = \frac{a}{n^k},$$

$$\cos (k - 1)\varphi = \frac{b}{n^{k-1}},$$

where a and b are integers relatively prime to n. Hence, by equation (18) we obtain

$$\cos (k + 1)\varphi = \frac{2}{n}\frac{a}{n^k} - \frac{b}{n^{k-1}}$$

$$= \frac{2a - bn^2}{n^{k+1}}.$$

Since neither the number a nor the number 2 has a factor in common with n, the numerator $2a - bn^2$ is relatively prime to n. This completes the induction.

Case 2. Suppose n is even, so that $n = 2m$ for some integer m. In this case cos $k\varphi$ can be expressed as a fraction whose denominator is of the form $2m^k$ and whose numerator is relatively prime to m (this is shown by induction in much the same way as in Case 1). Therefore, for $k > 0$, the denominator does not divide the numerator without leaving a nonzero remainder.

[1] Only this case (specifically, $n = 3$) is used in the proof of the theorem of Dehn.

THE THEOREM OF DEHN. *A cube and a regular tetrahedron having the same volume are not equidecomposable.*

Proof. In the regular tetrahedron $ABCD$ let us draw the altitude DE from the point D (Fig. 48). The point E lies at the centroid of the equilateral triangle ABC, so that the line AF which passes through the point E is a median. Therefore, F is the midpoint of the edge BC, and the line segment DF is a median of the triangle BCD. The length of the line segment EF is one third that of the median AF as well as of the median DF, that is,

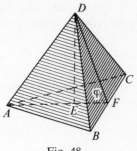

Fig. 48

$$\frac{EF}{DF} = \frac{1}{3}.$$

Thus, if we denote the angle F of the right triangle DEF by φ (that is, the dihedral angle of the tetrahedron $ABCD$), we obtain

$$\cos \varphi = \frac{1}{3}. \tag{19}$$

We now apply the theorem of Hadwiger. Each dihedral angle of a cube A is equal to $\frac{\pi}{2}$. Let us denote the dihedral angle of the regular tetrahedron B by φ. The numbers (13) of the theorem of Hadwiger will be

$$\pi, \frac{\pi}{2}, \varphi. \tag{20}$$

Let us find out what linear dependences exist between these numbers. Suppose

$$n_1\pi + n_2\frac{\pi}{2} + n_3\varphi = 0, \tag{21}$$

where n_1, n_2, and n_3 are integers, is a linear dependence between the numbers in (20); then

$$(2n_1 + n_2)\,\pi + 2n_3\varphi = 0.$$

Thus, we obtain a linear dependence between the numbers π and φ. But according to Lemma 15, such a linear dependence cannot exist, because φ and π are incommensurable (because of (19)).

Therefore, we have $2n_1 + n_2 = 0$, $n_3 = 0$, so that equation (21) takes on the form

$$n_1\pi + (-2n_1)\frac{\pi}{2} = 0. \tag{22}$$

No other linear dependence exists between the numbers (20). Let us take

$$f(\pi) = f\left(\frac{\pi}{2}\right) = 0, \quad f(\varphi) = 1. \tag{23}$$

This gives an additive function defined for the numbers (20). In fact, for an arbitrary linear dependence between the numbers (20), that is, for the equation (22), we have an analogous linear dependence between the numbers (23):

$$n_1 f(\pi) + (-2n_1) f\left(\frac{\pi}{2}\right) = 0.$$

Thus, we have an additive function defined for the numbers (20), which satisfies condition (15). In order to complete the proof of the nonequidecomposability of the cube and the regular tetrahedron, it now remains to show that (16) holds.

The cube A has twelve edges. Let the length of an edge be l. Then for the cube A the invariant $f(A)$ has the value

$$f(A) = 12lf\left(\frac{\pi}{2}\right) = 0$$

(see (23)). Let m denote the length of an edge of the regular tetrahedron B. Then the invariant $f(B)$ of the tetrahedron B will have the form

$$f(B) = 6mf(\varphi) \neq 0$$

(see (23)). Hence, $f(A) \neq f(B)$, so that the cube A and the tetrahedron B are not equidecomposable. Thus, the theorem of Dehn is proved.

16. PROOF OF THE THEOREM OF HADWIGER

We have not yet proved the theorem of Hadwiger. We shall now proceed with this proof.

LEMMA 16. *Let*

$$\alpha_1, \alpha_2, \ldots, \alpha_k \tag{24}$$

and

$$\gamma_1, \gamma_2, \ldots, \gamma_l \tag{25}$$

be real numbers, and let

$$f(\alpha_1), f(\alpha_2), \ldots, f(\alpha_k) \tag{26}$$

be an additive function for the numbers (24). *Then it is possible to find numbers*

$$f(\gamma_1), f(\gamma_2), \ldots, f(\gamma_l) \tag{27}$$

such that the numbers (26) *and* (27) *give an additive function for the numbers* (24) *and* (25) *taken together. In other words, any additive function for the numbers* (24) *can be extended to give an additive function for the numbers* (24) *and* (25).

It suffices to examine the case in which $l = 1$, that is, the case in which only one number γ is adjoined to the set of numbers (24) (since the numbers (25) can be adjoined to the set of numbers (24) one by one). So suppose an additive function (26) for the numbers (24) is given, and let γ be any real number. We must define a number $f(\gamma)$ so that the system of numbers

$$f(\alpha_1), f(\alpha_2), \ldots, f(\alpha_k), f(\gamma) \tag{28}$$

defines an additive function for the numbers

$$\alpha_1, \alpha_2, \ldots, \alpha_k, \gamma. \tag{29}$$

We carry out the proof by examining the following two cases.
Case 1. There exists no linear dependence

$$n_1\alpha_1 + n_2\alpha_2 + \cdots + n_k\alpha_k + n\gamma = 0$$

for the numbers (29) in which the coefficient n of γ is different from zero. In this case we may choose for the value of $f(\gamma)$ any arbitrary real number.
Case 2. There exists a linear dependence

$$n_1'\alpha_1 + n_2'\alpha_2 + \cdots + n_k'\alpha_k + n'\gamma = 0, n' \neq 0, \tag{30}$$

for the numbers (29). In this case we determine the number $f(\gamma)$ from the relationship

$$n_1'f(\alpha_1) + n_2'f(\alpha_2) + \cdots + n_k'f(\alpha_k) + n'f(\gamma) = 0. \tag{31}$$

From (31) we have

$$f(\gamma) = -\frac{n_1'}{n'}f(\alpha_1) - \frac{n_2'}{n'}f(\alpha_2) - \cdots - \frac{n_k'}{n'}f(\alpha_k).$$

Let us show that in this way we obtain an additive function of the numbers (29). Let

$$n_1\alpha_1 + n_2\alpha_2 + \cdots + n_k\alpha_k + n\gamma = 0 \qquad (32)$$

be an arbitrary linear dependence between the numbers (29) (different from or perhaps the same as (30)). We must show that then an analogous linear dependence exists between the numbers (28), that is, that we have

$$n_1f(\alpha_1) + n_2f(\alpha_2) + \cdots + n_kf(\alpha_k) + nf(\gamma) = 0. \qquad (33)$$

This can be shown as follows. Let us multiply both sides of equation (32) by n' and from the resulting equation subtract the equation (30) multiplied by n:

$$(n'n_1 - nn_1')\,\alpha_1 + (n'n_2 - nn_2')\,\alpha_2 + \cdots + (n'n_k - nn_k')\,\alpha_k = 0.$$

We then obtain a linear dependence between the numbers (24), and since (26) is an additive function for these numbers, the relationship

$$(n'n_1 - nn_1')f(\alpha_1) + (n'n_2 - nn_2')f(\alpha_2) + \cdots + (n'n_k - nn_k')f(\alpha_k) = 0$$

holds. Adding to this equation the equation (31) multiplied by n, we find that

$$n'n_1f(\alpha_1) + n'n_2f(\alpha_2) + \cdots + n'n_kf(\alpha_k) + n'nf(\gamma) = 0.$$

Finally, since $n' \neq 0$, we can divide this last equation by n', thereby obtaining (33). Thus, the numbers (28) give us an additive function for the numbers (29).

LEMMA 17. *Let A be a polyhedron decomposed into a finite number of smaller polyhedra $M_1, M_2, \ldots, M_k$. Let us denote all the different dihedral angles of the polyhedron A by*

$$\alpha_1, \alpha_2, \ldots, \alpha_p \qquad (34)$$

and all the different dihedral angles of the polyhedra $M_1, M_2, \ldots, M_k$ by

$$\gamma_1, \gamma_2, \ldots, \gamma_r. \qquad (35)$$

Let us adjoin π to the set of numbers (34) *and* (35) *and assume that for the set of numbers obtained*

$$\pi, \alpha_1, \alpha_2, \ldots, \alpha_p, \gamma_1, \gamma_2, \ldots, \gamma_r, \tag{36}$$

there is an additive function given:

$$f(\pi), f(\alpha_1), f(\alpha_2), \ldots, f(\alpha_p), f(\gamma_1), f(\gamma_2), \ldots, f(\gamma_r) \tag{37}$$

such that

$$f(\pi) = 0. \tag{38}$$

Then the invariants

$$f(A), f(M_1), f(M_2), \ldots, f(M_k)$$

for the polyhedra in question satisfy the equation

$$f(A) = f(M_1) + f(M_2) + \cdots + f(M_k). \tag{39}$$

To prove this, let us examine all line segments which are edges of the polyhedra $A, M_1, M_2, \ldots, M_k$. On these line segments we mark off all the points which are vertices of the polyhedra $A, M_1, M_2, \ldots, M_k$, and also all the points at which these edges intersect one another. We then obtain a finite number of shorter line segments. These shorter line segments we shall call *links*. A decomposition of a cube into smaller polyhedra is pictured in Fig. 49; in

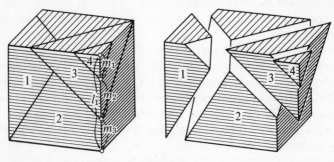

Fig. 49

this figure the edge of the cube labeled l_1 consists of the three links m_1, m_2, m_3. In general, each edge of each of the polyhedra $A, M_1, M_2, \ldots, M_k$ consists of one or of several links. Each link of the polyhedron A (that is, each link lying on one of the edges of the

47

polyhedron A) is also a link of one or of several of the polyhedra M_1, M_2, ..., M_k. Let us take an arbitrary link of the polyhedron A; let its length be m, and let α be the corresponding dihedral angle of the polyhedron A. Then α will be one of the numbers (34), so that $f(\alpha)$ is defined. Let us call the product $m \cdot f(\alpha)$ the *weight* of the link in question in the polyhedron A. In an analogous fashion we define the weights of the links in the polyhedra M_1, M_2, ..., M_k. We should note that one and the same link may have different weights in different polyhedra adjoining it; for at this link the adjoining polyhedra may have different dihedral angles.

Let us now take all the links of the polyhedron A, find their weight in the polyhedron A, and compute the sum of all these weights. It is easy to see that this sum is just the invariant $f(A)$ of the polyhedron A. For concreteness, let us consider the edge l_1 of the polyhedron A and suppose it consists of the three links m_1, m_2, m_3 (Fig. 49). Then one and the same dihedral angle α_1 of the polyhedron A, namely the dihedral angle at the edge l_1, will correspond to each of the links m_1, m_2, m_3. The sum of the weights of the links m_1, m_2, m_3 is, therefore,

$$m_1 f(\alpha_1) + m_2 f(\alpha_1) + m_3 f(\alpha_1) = (m_1 + m_2 + m_3)f(\alpha_1) = l_1 f(\alpha_1).$$

Analogously, the sum of the weights of all the links making up the edge l_2 of the polyhedron A is equal to $l_2 f(\alpha_2)$, and so on. The sum of the weights of all the links of the polyhedron A thus coincides with the sum (12); that is, it is equal to the invariant $f(A)$ of the polyhedron A.

Similarly, the invariant of each of the polyhedra M_1, M_2, ..., M_k is equal to the sum of the weights of all its links. (Of course, the weight of each link is calculated for the polyhedron in question.)

We are now in a position to establish the validity of the relationship (39). To calculate the sum found on the right-hand side of this equation, we must calculate the sum of the weights of all the links in each of the polyhedra M_1, M_2, ..., M_k. Let us find the coefficient with which a link m enters into this sum. Let the dihedral angles of the polyhedra M_1, M_2, ..., M_k adjoining the link m be denoted by

$$\gamma_i, \gamma_j, \ldots, \gamma_s.$$

(These numbers are included among the numbers (35).) Then the weight of the link in question in the polyhedron with the dihedral angle γ_i is $mf(\gamma_i)$; its weight in the polyhedron with the dihedral angle γ_j is $mf(\gamma_j)$; and so on. Thus, the sum of the weights of all the links m in the polyhedra $M_1, M_2, \ldots, M_k$ which adjoin the link m is given by

$$mf(\gamma_i) + mf(\gamma_j) + \cdots + mf(\gamma_s). \qquad (40)$$

Each of the links will be one of the following three types:

(1) Those links which are situated completely in the interior of the polyhedron A (with the possible exception of their end points). If m is such a link and if each of the polyhedra $M_1, M_2, \ldots, M_k$ which adjoin the line segment m has this line segment as a link, then all the dihedral angles of the polyhedra which adjoin the link m add up to 2π. (See Fig. 50a; in this figure, as also in Fig. 50b, 51, 52a, 52b, the decomposition of the polyhedron A and of the

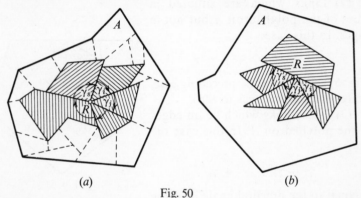

(a)   (b)

Fig. 50

polyhedra adjoining the line segment m is represented in a plane perpendicular to the link m; the link m itself is represented in these figures by the point R.) Thus, in this case $\gamma_i + \gamma_j + \cdots + \gamma_s = 2\pi$, or

$$\gamma_i + \gamma_j + \cdots + \gamma_s - 2\pi = 0.$$

This is a linear dependence between the numbers (36) and we, therefore, have

$$f(\gamma_i) + f(\gamma_j) + \cdots + f(\gamma_s) - 2f(\pi) = 0.$$

Using (38), the latter equation reduces to

$$f(\gamma_i) + f(\gamma_j) + \cdots + f(\gamma_s) = 0,$$

so that the expression (40) reduces to zero.

If m is a link situated in the interior of the polyhedron A, and is one of the polyhedra $M_1, M_2, \ldots, M_k$ which adjoin the line segment *m fails to have this line segment as a link*[1] (which is to say that the line segment m lies in the plane of one of the faces of one of the polyhedra $M_1, M_2, \ldots, M_k$), then the dihedral angles of the remaining polyhedra which adjoin the line segment m add up to a straight angle (Fig. 50b):

$$\gamma_i + \gamma_j + \cdots + \gamma_s = \pi.$$

Hence, it follows (as above) that the expression (40) reduces to zero.

Thus, links which are situated in the interior of the polyhedron A may be neglected in the calculation of the right-hand side of the equality (39), since the sum of their weights is equal to zero.

(2) Links which are situated in faces of the polyhedron A but not in edges. In this case

$$\gamma_i + \gamma_j + \cdots + \gamma_s = \pi$$

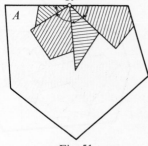

Fig. 51

(Fig. 51), and, as in the preceding case, expression (40) reduces to zero.

(3) Those links which lie on edges of the polyhedron A. In this case the sum

$$\gamma_i + \gamma_j + \cdots + \gamma_s$$

is equal to the dihedral angle α of the corresponding edge:

$$\gamma_i + \gamma_j + \cdots + \gamma_s = \alpha$$

(Fig. 52a), or else it is equal to the angle $\alpha - \pi$; that is,

$$\gamma_i + \gamma_j + \cdots + \gamma_s = \alpha - \pi;$$

this may occur if the angle α is greater than π—see Fig. 52b. In either case we have

$$f(\gamma_i) + f(\gamma_j) + \cdots + f(\gamma_s) = f(\alpha),$$

---

[1] If two polyhedra which adjoin the line segment m do not have it as a link, that is, if m lies within the face of two adjoining polyhedra, then these two polyhedra alone will adjoin the segment m; then m does not lie on an edge of the polyhedra $M_1, M_2, \ldots, M_k$ and, therefore, is not a link.

and the expression (40) is equal to $mf(\alpha)$, which is the weight of the link in question in the polyhedron A. Thus, the sum appearing

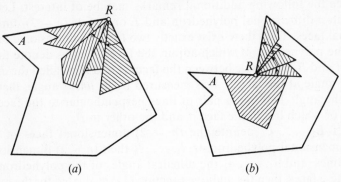

(a)   (b)

Fig. 52

on the right-hand side of equation (39) is equal to the sum of the weights of all the links of the polyhedron A, that is, to the invariant $f(A)$.

Proof of the theorem of Hadwiger. Let the polyhedra A and B be equidecomposable, and let $M_1, M_2, \ldots, M_n$ be polyhedra which can be arranged so as to give either A or B. Let the internal dihedral angles of all the polyhedra $M_1, M_2, \ldots, M_n$ be $\gamma_1, \gamma_2, \ldots, \gamma_r$. In accordance with Lemma 16, the additive function (14) can be extended to give an additive function for the numbers

$$\pi, \alpha_1, \alpha_2, \ldots, \alpha_p, \beta_1, \beta_2, \ldots, \beta_q, \gamma_1, \gamma_2, \ldots, \gamma_r.$$

(As before, this additive function satisfies condition (15).) Since the polyhedron A consists of the polyhedra $M_1, M_2, \ldots, M_n$, the invariant $f(A)$ has the value

$$f(A) = f(M_1) + f(M_2) + \cdots + f(M_n)$$

(Lemma 17). But the polyhedron B can also be obtained as an arrangement of the polyhedra $M_1, M_2, \ldots, M_n$, so that

$$f(B) = f(M_1) + f(M_2) + \cdots + f(M_n).$$

But then $f(A) = f(B)$, which contradicts equation (16). Hence, the assumption that the polyhedra A and B are equidecomposable leads to a contradiction.

51

17. n-DIMENSIONAL POLYHEDRA

For the reader who is familiar with the concept of n-dimensional space the following additional remarks may be of interest. Let M be an n-dimensional polyhedron and L one of its $(n - 2)$-dimensional faces. Then there exist exactly two $(n - 1)$-dimensional faces of the polyhedron M which adjoin the face L; let us denote these by A and B. The angle between the faces A and B is called the *dihedral* angle at the face L. It is measured by its *linear* angle, that is, by the angle between a pair of lines perpendicular to the face L, one of which lies in the face A and the other in B.

If $L_1, \ldots, L_k$ denote the $(n - 2)$-dimensional faces of the n-dimensional polyhedron M, $l_1, \ldots, l_k$ their $(n - 2)$-dimensional volumes, and $\alpha_1, \ldots, \alpha_k$ the dihedral angles of the polyhedron M at these faces, then the additive function (11) evaluated for the numbers $\alpha_1, \ldots, \alpha_k$ (see page 40) can be used to define the sum (12), which we shall call the *invariant* of the polyhedron M. With this definition of the invariant the theorem of Hadwiger, together with its proof, is valid for n-dimensional polyhedra (see [4]).

The theorem of Dehn is also readily generalized. A regular n-dimensional pyramid (simplex) has dihedral angles which are equal to $\cos^{-1} \dfrac{1}{n}$. (The reader can easily convince himself of this by means of an inductive argument that is completely analogous to that given in section 15.) From this it follows, with the aid of Lemma 15, that for $n > 3$ a regular pyramid and a cube which have the same volume are not equidecomposable (see section 15).

6. Methods for Calculating Volumes

18. THE METHOD OF LIMITS

Let us recall our method for calculating areas of plane figures. After establishing the formula for the area of a rectangle, the calculation of the area of other polygons is carried out by applying either of two simple methods: the decomposition method or the complementation method. In plane geometry the method of limits is applied only in calculating areas of curvilinear figures.

When calculating the volumes of solid bodies, we sometimes use the decomposition or complementation method. For example, to prove that the volume of an oblique prism is equal to the product of the length of a side and the area of a perpendicular cross section, one may use either the decomposition method (Fig. 53) or the complementation method (Fig. 54). In other words, every oblique

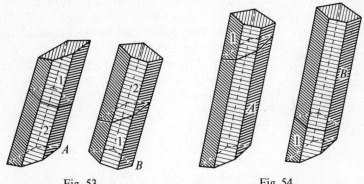

Fig. 53   Fig. 54

prism is equidecomposable (and equicomplementable) with a *right* prism, the length of whose lateral edges is the same as that of the given prism, and whose base is congruent to a perpendicular cross section of the given prism. Since each right prism is in turn equidecomposable (and equicomplementable) with a regular parallelepiped, we obtain the following theorem: *every oblique prism is equidecomposable (and equicomplementable) with a rectangular parallelepiped of the same volume.* Thus, both the decomposition method and the complementation method can be successfully applied to calculate the volume of any prism (whether right or oblique).

In calculating the volume of a pyramid, however, neither of these two methods is used. Instead, use is made of the *method of limits*: a series of rather complex stair-shaped solids is examined (Fig. 55), and one then passes to the limit by an infinitely large number of small steps (a "devil's staircase"). What have we here? Could it be that up until now mathematicians simply have not been lucky enough to find a simple formula for the volume of a pyramid by using the decomposition or complementation methods? This is not the case: these methods are altogether inadequate for establishing a formula for the volume of a pyramid. To obtain such a formula, the application of a more complex method (the method of limits) is unavoidable.

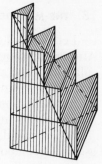

Fig. 55

In order to be convinced of this, let us recall briefly the usual procedure for calculating the volume of a pyramid. Let $ABCD$ be a tetrahedron, and let us construct an oblique triangular prism $ABCDEF$ whose base is ABC and whose lateral edge is AD (Fig.

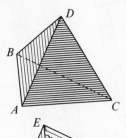

56). This prism can be decomposed into three tetrahedra $ABCD$, $BCDE$, $CDEF$ (Fig. 57), which we shall denote, for the sake of brevity, by M_1, M_2, M_3. It is easy to show that any two of the pyramids M_1, M_2, M_3 have congruent bases and equal

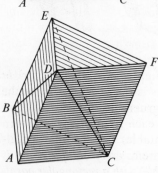

Fig. 56

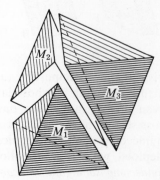

Fig. 57

altitudes. Thus, it remains to prove that *two pyramids having congruent bases and equal altitudes are equal in volume*. It is this proposition which is proved by the method of limits. We shall show that it is not possible to prove this fact by means of the decomposition method. To do this we show that there exists a pair of pyramids having congruent bases and equal altitudes, but whose invariants (see (12)) are different for some additive function f. From this it will follow, by virtue of the theorem of Hadwiger, that the two pyramids are not equidecomposable.

Let us turn again to Fig. 56 and 57 and assume that the pyramid M_1 (that is, the pyramid $ABCD$, which was used to construct the prism $ABCDEF$) is a regular pyramid, that is, a regular tetrahedron. According to Lemma 16 it is possible to extend the additive function (23) to an additive function for all dihedral angles of the pyramids M_1, M_2, M_3 and the prism $ABCDEF$. Thus, we find (Lemma 17) that the sum $f(M_1) + f(M_2) + f(M_3)$ is the invariant of the prism $ABCDEF$. Since this prism is equidecomposable with a rectangular parallelepiped (in which all dihedral angles are equal to $\frac{\pi}{2}$), the invariant of this prism is equal to zero. Thus, we have

$$f(M_1) + f(M_2) + f(M_3) = 0. \qquad (41)$$

We know already that the invariant $f(M_1)$ for the regular pyramid M_1 differs from zero. Hence, the equations

$$f(M_1) = f(M_2) = f(M_3)$$

cannot hold; for if they did hold, they would contradict formula (41). Thus, among the pyramids M_1, M_2, M_3 there is a pair whose invariants are different, and hence a pair which are not equidecomposable (by the theorem of Hadwiger). Thus, we have shown that there exists a pair of pyramids having congruent bases and equal altitudes which are not equidecomposable.

It is now clear that the decomposition method does not enable us to calculate the volume of a pyramid. What about the complementation method? Its inapplicability is established once and for all by the following proposition.[1]

THEOREM. *If two polyhedra A and B satisfy the conditions of Hadwiger's theorem, then they are not equicomplementable.*

[1] The inapplicability of the complementation method follows also from the more general theorem of Sydler, the proof of which is given below.

Proof. Let us suppose the converse holds: there exist polyhedra $M_1, M_2, \ldots, M_n$ which can be adjoined to both A and B to give the same polyhedron C. According to Lemma 16 the additive function (14) can be extended to give an additive function for all dihedral angles of all the polyhedra $M_1, M_2, \ldots, M_n, C$. Applying Lemma 17, we obtain

$$f(C) = f(A) + f(M_1) + f(M_2) + \cdots + f(M_n),$$
$$f(C) = f(B) + f(M_1) + f(M_2) + \cdots + f(M_n).$$

But these equalities contradict the relationship (16). Therefore, the polyhedra A and B cannot be equicomplementable.

From this theorem it follows that a regular tetrahedron and a cube are not only nonequidecomposable but are, moreover, nonequicomplementable. Also, pairs of pyramids having congruent bases and equal altitudes but whose invariants are different are not equicomplementable. Since we have demonstrated the existence of such pairs of pyramids above, it is clear that the complementation method cannot be applied to calculate the volume of a pyramid.

19. EQUIVALENCE OF THE DECOMPOSITION AND COMPLEMENTATION METHODS (OPTIONAL)

In the first chapter of this booklet we saw that for plane polygons equidecomposability and equicomplementability have the same significance; that is, for plane polygons the decomposition and complementation methods are equivalent. The proof of this fact, given in Chapter 1, was based essentially upon the Bolyai-Gerwin theorem on the equidecomposability of pairs of polygons having equal areas. We know already that from the equality of the volumes of two polyhedra it does not follow that they are either equidecomposable or equicomplementable. Therefore, it is not possible to establish the equivalence of the decomposition and complementation methods for polyhedra by arguments analogous to those used in Chapter 1. The question of the equivalence of these methods for polyhedra is answered by the following theorem.

THEOREM OF SYDLER. *Two polyhedra are equicomplementable if and only if they are equidecomposable* (see [8]).

We shall now prove this theorem with the aid of several lemmas.

LEMMA 18. *If the polyhedra A and B are equidecomposable, they are also equicomplementable.*

Let M_1, M_2, ..., M_k be a series of polyhedra which can be arranged in such a way as to give either A or B. Assume, by translating B if necessary, that A and B have no point in common. Let M be a polyhedron containing the two polyhedra A and B in its interior, and let M_0 be that part of the polyhedron M which lies outside of the polyhedra A and B. It is readily seen that by using the polyhedra M_0, M_1, M_2, ..., M_k, it is possible to complement both A and B to give the same polyhedron M. In fact, by assembling the polyhedra M_1, M_2, ..., M_k to form the polyhedron A, we find that the polyhedra M_0, M_1, M_2, ..., M_k can be so arranged as to fill up the whole polyhedron M, with the exception of the polyhedron B; that is, these polyhedra complement B in the polyhedron M. By assembling the polyhedra M_1, M_2, ..., M_k to form the polyhedron B, we find that the polyhedron A can be complemented by the polyhedra M_0, M_1, M_2, ..., M_k to give the polyhedron M. Thus, A and B are equicomplementable.

We note that the polyhedron M_0 is just the polyhedron M with two hollow spaces in the shape of the polyhedra A and B. If the reader does not regard M_0 as a "polyhedron," then this solid can be "decomposed" into several polyhedra not containing "empty spaces" in order to complete the proof.

LEMMA 19. *All pairs of prisms which are equal in volume are equidecomposable.*

We note first of all that if the bases of two prisms are of equal area and lie in parallel planes, and if the generators of the prisms are equal and parallel (Fig. 58), then these prisms will be equide-

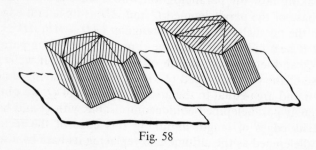

Fig. 58

composable; for by the Bolyai-Gerwin theorem, their bases are equidecomposable.

From this it follows that every prism is equidecomposable with some (generally oblique) parallelepiped.

Furthermore, every oblique parallelepiped is equidecomposable with some rectangular parallelepiped. Let p be the plane of the base of an oblique parallelepiped P, A a point of this plane, and AB a line segment equal and parallel to the lateral edge of the parallelepiped P (Fig. 59). Also, let l be the projection of the straight line AB onto the plane p, and let m be a straight line in the plane p perpendicular to l and passing through the point A.

On lines l and m choose points C and D such that the rectangle whose sides are AC and AD is equal in area with the base of the parallelepiped P, and with this rectangle as base construct the paral-

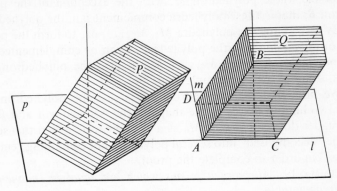

Fig. 59

lelepiped Q with lateral edge AB. Then on the basis of what has been said above, the parallelepipeds P and Q are equidecomposable. Taking now the parallelogram whose sides are AB and AC as the base of the parallelepiped Q and AD as its lateral edge, we see that the parallelepiped Q is rectangular ($AD \perp AB$, $AD \perp AC$).

Let K be a cube which has the same volume as the parallelepiped Q, and let a be the length of the edges of K. If we replace the base of the parallelepiped Q with a rectangle having a side of length a and area equal to the area of the base of Q, we obtain a rectangular parallelepiped equidecomposable with Q and having one of its edges of length a. Taking this edge of the rectangular parallelepiped as the altitude and replacing its base by a square of the same area, we obtain the cube K.

Thus, every prism is equidecomposable with a cube of equal volume; it follows that two prisms of equal volume are equidecomposable.

Before proceeding to the formulation of the next lemmas, we should settle some matters pertaining to notation. Let A and B be two polyhedra which do not have any of their interior points in common. The single polyhedron which occupies all the space occupied by A and B together we shall denote by $A + B$. The "sum" of more than two polyhedra is defined analogously. In particular, if the polyhedron A is decomposed into the polyhedra M_1, $M_2, \ldots, M_k$, we shall express this fact by writing $A = M_1 + M_2 + \cdots + M_k$. Further, if each of the n polyhedra $M_1, M_2, \ldots, M_n$ is congruent to the polyhedron M, we abbreviate the above notation for their sum by the expression nM. A polyhedron which is similar to the polyhedron M and whose coefficient of similarity is λ, we shall denote by $M^{(\lambda)}$. Finally, we shall use the symbol $\sim$ to indicate the equidecomposability of polyhedra; thus, the notation $A \sim B$ means that the polyhedra A and B are equidecomposable.

LEMMA 20. *Let* $P_1, P_2, \ldots, P_k$ *be a sequence of prisms having no common interior points, and let* P *be a prism whose volume is the sum of the volumes of* $P_1, P_2, \ldots, P_k$. *Then*

$$P_1 + P_2 + \cdots + P_k \sim P.$$

In order to prove this lemma, replace the prisms $P_1, P_2, \ldots, P_k$ by rectangular parallelepipeds $\Pi_1, \Pi_2, \ldots, \Pi_k$ all having congruent bases but having volumes equal to the volumes of the prisms P_1, $P_2, \ldots, P_k$, respectively. Next, place these new parallelepipeds one on top of the other (Fig. 60). In this way we obtain a large paral-

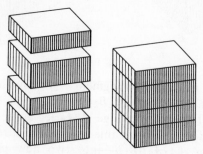

Fig. 60

lelepiped Π; since the volume of Π is just the volume of the prism P, we obtain (see Lemma 19)

$$P_1 + P_2 + \cdots + P_k \sim \Pi_1 + \Pi_2 + \cdots + \Pi_k \sim \Pi \sim P.$$

59

LEMMA 21. *Let M be an arbitrary polyhedron and n a natural number. Then for some prism P we have*

$$M^{(n)} \sim P + nM.$$

We shall prove this lemma first of all on the assumption that M is a tetrahedron. In this case $M^{(n)}$ is also a tetrahedron whose altitude will be n times that of M.

Divide the altitude of $M^{(n)}$ into n equal parts, and through each division point pass a plane parallel to the base. This divides $M^{(n)}$ into n "layers," the topmost of which is a tetrahedron congruent to M (Fig. 61). Consider any layer below the top one. It is a frustum of a pyramid; we shall denote its lower and upper

Fig. 61

bases by ABC and $A_1B_1C_1$. Through the edge A_1B_1 of the upper base pass a plane parallel to the edge CC_1 (Fig. 62). It intersects

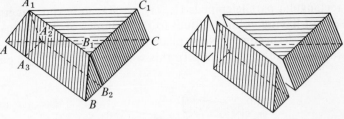

Fig. 62

the lower base along a line segment A_2B_2, dividing the frustum into two parts, the prism $A_2B_2CA_1B_1C_1$ and the polyhedron $AA_1A_2BB_1B_2$. Through the edge A_1A_2 let us now pass a plane parallel to the face BB_1B_2 of this latter polyhedron. This divides the polyhedron $AA_1A_2BB_1B_2$ into two new parts, the prism $A_1A_2A_3B_1B_2B$ and the tetrahedron $AA_1A_2A_3$, which, as is readily seen, is congruent to the tetrahedron M (for, it is similar to M and has the same altitude). Thus, each layer, except for the topmost one, can be decomposed into a tetrahedron congruent to M and two prisms. The whole tetrahedron $M^{(n)}$ consists of n tetrahedra congruent to M, and a series of prisms. By Lemma 20 these prisms may be replaced by a single prism P, and we obtain

$$M^{(n)} \sim P + nM,$$

which shows that the lemma holds if M is a tetrahedron.

Now let M be an arbitrary polyhedron. If it is not convex, we decompose it into a finite number of convex polyhedra by drawing in all the planes that contain faces of M. Further, each convex polyhedron can be decomposed into pyramids; to do this it is sufficient to take a point O in the interior of the polyhedron and to consider all the pyramids whose common vertex is the point O and

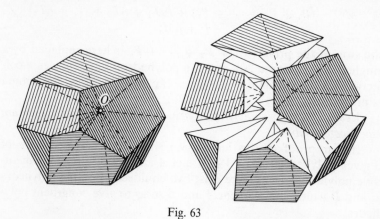

Fig. 63

whose bases are faces of the polyhedron (Fig. 63). Finally, every pyramid can be decomposed into several tetrahedra (Fig. 64). Thus,

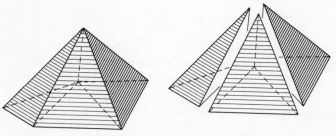

Fig. 64

every polyhedron can be decomposed into a finite number of tetrahedra. Let

$$M = T_1 + T_2 + \cdots + T_k \qquad (42)$$

be such a decomposition. By enlarging all these solids by the factor n, we obtain

$$M^{(n)} = T_1^{(n)} + T_2^{(n)} + \cdots + T_k^{(n)}.$$

By what has been proved above, we have

$$T_1^{(n)} \sim P_1 + nT_1, \quad T_2^{(n)} \sim P_2 + nT_2, \ldots, T_k^{(n)} \sim P_k + nT_k,$$

where $P_1, P_2, \ldots, P_k$ is a series of prisms. Thus,

$$M^{(n)} \sim (P_1 + P_2 + \cdots + P_k) + (nT_1 + nT_2 + \cdots + nT_k)$$
$$\sim P + nM;$$

the sum of the prisms $P_1 + P_2 + \cdots + P_k$ is here replaced by a single prism (Lemma 20), and the polyhedron nM replaces n collections of the pyramids $T_1, T_2, \ldots, T_k$, by (42). Thus, the lemma is proved.

LEMMA 22. *If two polyhedra are equicomplementable, they are equidecomposable.*

In our proof of this lemma we shall denote the volume of a given polyhedron M by $V(M)$. Let A and B be equicomplementable polyhedra. Then there exist two equidecomposable polyhedra C and D which complement A and B so as to give congruent polyhedra:

$$A + C \cong B + D, \quad C \sim D. \qquad (43)$$

Let C_1 be a cube such that it is possible to place the polyhedron C into its interior, and let n be a whole number greater than

$\sqrt{1 + \dfrac{V(C_1)}{V(A)}}$. Then $n^2 > 1 + \dfrac{V(C_1)}{V(A)}$, or $n^2 V(A) > V(A) + V(C_1)$.

Multiplying both sides of this inequality by n and noting that $n^3 V(A)$ is the volume of the polyhedron $A^{(n)}$, we can write

$$V(A^{(n)}) > nV(A) + nV(C_1). \qquad (44)$$

Furthermore, according to Lemma 21, we have

$$A^{(n)} \sim P + nA, \quad B^{(n)} \sim Q + nB, \qquad (45)$$

where P and Q are prisms; the first of these relationships gives

$V(A^{(n)}) = V(P) + nV(A)$. From this equality and from (44) it follows that $V(P) > nV(C_1)$; that is, the volume of the prism P is more than n times the volume of the cube C_1. By Lemma 19 we may assume that P is a rectangular parallelepiped with the same base as the cube C_1. Then the altitude of the parallelepiped P is at least n times the altitude of the cube C_1, so that it is possible to place inside P, n cubes congruent to C_1; *a fortiori* it is possible to place inside P, n polyhedra congruent to C. Place in P the figure nC. The remaining part of the parallelepiped P (not taken up by the figure nC) let us call T:

$$P = T + nC. \tag{46}$$

Furthermore, the prisms P and Q are equal in volume (since $V(A) = V(B)$, $V(A^{(n)}) = V(B^{(n)})$, so that by (45) we have $V(P) = V(Q)$); consequently, prisms P and Q are equidecomposable (Lemma 19):

$$P \sim Q. \tag{47}$$

A comparison of the relationships (43) and (45) with (47) shows that

$$A^{(n)} \sim P + nA = T + nC + nA = T + n(A + C) \sim T + n(B + D)$$
$$= T + nB + nD \sim T + nB + nC$$
$$= (T + nC) + nB \sim P + nB \sim Q + nB \sim B^{(n)}.$$

Thus, the polyhedra $A^{(n)}$ and $B^{(n)}$ are equidecomposable; that is, they can be decomposed into corresponding congruent parts. By contracting both of the polyhedra $A^{(n)}$ and $B^{(n)}$ to $\frac{1}{n}$ of their size, we find that the polyhedra A and B are also equidecomposable. Thus, the lemma is proved.

It remains to remark that the theorem of Sydler is equivalent to Lemmas 18 and 22.

Appendix

1. NECESSARY AND SUFFICIENT CONDITIONS FOR THE EQUIDECOMPOSABILITY OF POLYHEDRA

We shall now give (without proof) the conditions for equide-composability of polyhedra given in a paper of Hadwiger (see [6]). Assume that for each polyhedron A there is a corresponding number $\chi(A)$ which fulfills the following conditions:

(1) To congruent polyhedra A and B correspond equal numbers $\chi(A) = \chi(B)$ (the condition of invariance);

(2) If the polyhedron A is decomposed into several polyhedra $M_1, M_2, \ldots, M_k$, then the equation

$$\chi(A) = \chi(M_1) + \chi(M_2) + \cdots + \chi(M_k)$$

holds (the condition of additivity);

(3) If $A^{(\lambda)}$ is a polyhedron similar to the polyhedron A and with coefficient of similarity λ, then $\chi(A^{(\lambda)}) = \lambda \cdot \chi(A)$ (the condition of linearity).

Under these conditions we say that χ is a *linear additive invariant*. The following theorem holds:

THEOREM. *For two polyhedra A and B to be equidecomposable it is necessary and sufficient that their volumes be equal and that $\chi(A) = \chi(B)$ for every linear additive invariant χ.*

In other words, if the polyhedra A and B have equal volumes but are not equidecomposable, then there exists a linear additive invariant χ for which $\chi(A) \neq \chi(B)$. We note that by Sydler's theorem (proved above), this is also a necessary and sufficient condition for the polyhedra A and B to be equicomplementable.

It is interesting to compare this condition with the formulation of Hadwiger's theorem proved earlier (section 16). There we also used an invariant $f(A)$. Congruent polyhedra A and B had equal invariants: $f(A) = f(B)$. This invariant was additive (Lemma 17). It was also linear (since the lengths of the edges of the polyhedron $A^{(\lambda)}$ were equal to λ times the lengths of the edges of the polyhe-dron A), and, since their dihedral angles were equal, it follows that

$f(A^{(\lambda)}) = \lambda \cdot f(A)$ (using the definition of the additive invariant f given in section 14). Nevertheless, the invariant f differs from the invariants in the theorem stated above: the invariant f is not defined for all polyhedra. It is defined for only the two polyhedra mentioned in the theorem of Hadwiger, and when we encountered other polyhedra (in Lemma 17) we gave a new definition for the values of the invariant f for those polyhedra.

It should be noted that the proof of the existence of linear additive invariants defined simultaneously for *all* polyhedra is essentially *nonelementary*. In order to derive such invariants[1] (and also to prove the theorem formulated above), we make use of so-called *transfinite induction,* the study of which is beyond the scope of this booklet.

2. G-EQUIDECOMPOSABILITY OF POLYHEDRA

As in the case of polygons, it is possible to speak of G-equidecomposable polyhedra, where G is some group of motions. (It must, of course, be understood that here we are talking about motions of *solid* figures, particularly polyhedra.) Let T be the group consisting of all the parallel translations in space. We may then pose the question as to whether or not two polyhedra are T-equidecomposable. We note the following interesting theorem, which has also been proved by Hadwiger (see [7]).

THEOREM. *In order that a convex polyhedron be T-equidecomposable with a cube, it is necessary and sufficient that each of its faces be a centrally symmetric polygon.*[2]

From this it follows that two polyhedra of equal volume, each having faces which are centrally symmetric, are mutually T-equidecomposable. In particular, if we consider two congruent polyhedra with centrally symmetric faces, then in whatever manner they are rotated in relation to each other they will always be T-equidecomposable.

Along with G-equidecomposability we may also examine G-equicomplementability of polyhedra (G being a group of mo-

---

[1] Only one invariant exists which has an elementary definition; this is the invariant which has the value zero for every polyhedron A. However, it is pointless to discuss this invariant.

[2] From the results obtained by the Soviet geometer A. D. Alexandroff it follows that a polyhedron having this property is itself centrally symmetric.

tions). If the group G contains all parallel translations (it may, in addition to translations, also contain other motions), two polyhedra will be G-equicomplementable if and only if they are G-equidecomposable. The proof for this theorem (which is valid also for n-dimensional space) can be obtained by making only slight modifications in the proof of the theorem of Sydler given above (see [5]).

Bibliography

The following are the original research papers in which the material of this booklet is developed.

1. Dehn, M. "Ueber den Rauminhalt," *Math. Ann.* 55 (1902), pp. 465–478.
2. Hadwiger, H., and Glur, P. "Zerlegungsgleichheit ebener Polygone," *Elem. der Math.* 6 (1951), pp. 97–106.
3. Hadwiger, H. "Zum Problem der Zerlegungsgleichheit der Polyeder," *Archiv der Math.* 2 (1949–1950), pp. 441–444.
4. Hadwiger, H. "Zum Problem der Zerlegungsgleichheit k-dimensionaler Polyeder," *Math. Ann.* 127 (1954), pp. 170–174.
5. Hadwiger, H. "Ergänzungsgleichheit k-dimensionaler Polyeder," *Math. Zeit.* 55 (1952), pp. 292–298.
6. Hadwiger, H. "Zerlegungsgleichheit und additive Polyederfunktionale," *Archiv der Math.* 1 (1948–1949), pp. 468–472.
7. Hadwiger, H. "Mittelpunktspolyeder und translative Zerlegungsgleichheit," *Math. Nachr.* 8 (1952), pp. 53–58.
8. Sydler, J. P. "Sur la décomposition des polyèdres," *Comm. Math. Helv.* 16 (1943–1944), pp. 266–273.

The following books and articles contain more popular expositions of geometric dissection problems.

9. Cundy, H. M., and Rollett, A. P. *Mathematical Models.* Oxford: Clarendon Press, 1952. Chapter 2.
10. Dudeney, H. E. *Amusements in Mathematics.* New York: Dover Publications, Inc., 1958. Pp. 27–40.
11. Gardner, Martin. "Mathematical Games," *Scientific American,* November, 1961, pp. 158–169.
12. Lindgren, H. "Two Six-Piece Dissections," *The American Mathematical Monthly,* Vol. 64, No. 5 (May, 1957), pp. 368–369.
13. Lindgren, H. "Going One Better in Geometric Dissections," *Mathematical Gazette,* May, 1961, pp. 94–97.
14. The University of Chicago College Mathematics Staff, the following articles in *The Mathematics Teacher:*
    "A Problem on the Cutting of Squares," Vol. 49, No. 5 (May, 1956), pp. 332–343.
    "More on the Cutting of Squares," Vol. 49, No. 6 (October, 1956), pp. 442–454.

"Still More on the Cutting of Squares," Vol. 49, No. 8 (December, 1956), pp. 585–596.

"New Exercises in Plane Geometry," Vol. 50, No. 2 (February, 1957), pp. 125–135.

"More New Exercises in Plane Geometry," Vol. 50, No. 5 (May, 1957), pp. 330–339.

"Four More Exercises in Cutting Figures," Vol. 51, No. 2 (February, 1958), pp. 96–104.

TOPICS IN MATHEMATICS

Topics in Mathematics is a series of booklets translated and adapted from the Russian series *Popular Lectures in Mathematics*. These American editions have been prepared by the Survey of Recent East European Mathematical Literature at the University of Chicago under a grant from the National Science Foundation. These booklets provide students of mathematics at various levels, as well as other interested readers, with valuable supplementary material to further their mathematical knowledge and development.

This booklet, Equivalent and Equidecomposable Figures, deals with a class of problems fundamental to the theories of area and volume. The first four chapters deal with the question: If two polygons have equal areas, is it possible to dissect one of them into a finite number of parts which can be rearranged to form the other? The analogous question for polyhedra is discussed in the last two chapters. The first four chapters assume a background in plane geometry. Solid geometry and trigonometry are needed for the last two chapters.

The author, V. G. BOLTYANSKII, is a Professor at Moscow State University. He is an outstanding member of the younger generation of Russian mathematicians, having earned an international reputation for his research in topology and differential geometry. He is also actively concerned with mathematics education.